Probability

Between Never and Always

Grade 5

Also appropriate for Grade 6

Margie Singer
Cliff Konold
Andee Rubin

Developed at TERC, Cambridge, Massachusetts

Dale Seymour Publications®
White Plains, New York

The *Investigations* curriculum was developed at TERC (formerly
Technical Education Research Centers) in collaboration with Kent State
University and the State University of New York at Buffalo. The work was
supported in part by National Science Foundation Grant No. ESI-9050210.
TERC is a nonprofit company working to improve mathematics and science
education. TERC is located at 2067 Massachusetts Avenue, Cambridge,
MA 02140.

This project was supported, in part,
by the
National Science Foundation
Opinions expressed are those of the authors
and not necessarily those of the Foundation

Managing Editor: Catherine Anderson
Series Editor: Beverly Cory
Manuscript Editor: Nancy Tune
Revision Team: Laura Marshall Alavosus, Ellen Harding, Patty Green Holubar,
Suzanne Knot, Beverly Hersh Lozoff
ESL Consultant: Nancy Sokol Green
Production/Manufacturing Director: Janet Yearian
Production/Manufacturing Coordinator: Joe Conte
Design Manager: Jeff Kelly
Design: Don Taka
Illustrations: DJ Simison, Carl Yoshihara
Cover: Bay Graphics
Composition: Archetype Book Composition

This book is published by Dale Seymour Publications®, an imprint of
Addison Wesley Longman, Inc.

Dale Seymour Publications
10 Bank Street
White Plains, NY 10602
Customer Service: 1-800-872-1100

DALE
SEYMOUR
PUBLICATIONS®

Order number DS47046
ISBN 1-57232-799-5
2 3 4 5 6 7 8 9 10-ML-02 01 00 99 98

Printed on Recycled Paper

T E R C

Principal Investigator   Susan Jo Russell

Co-Principal Investigator   Cornelia Tierney

Director of Research and Evaluation   Jan Mokros

Curriculum Development

Joan Akers
Michael T. Battista
Mary Berle-Carman
Douglas H. Clements
Karen Economopoulos
Claryce Evans
Marlene Kliman
Cliff Konold
Jan Mokros
Megan Murray
Ricardo Nemirovsky
Tracy Noble
Andee Rubin
Susan Jo Russell
Margie Singer
Cornelia Tierney

Evaluation and Assessment

Mary Berle-Carman
Jan Mokros
Andee Rubin
Tracey Wright

Teacher Support

Kabba Colley
Karen Economopoulos
Anne Goodrow
Nancy Ishihara
Liana Laughlin
Jerrie Moffett
Megan Murray
Margie Singer
Dewi Win
Virginia Woolley
Tracey Wright
Lisa Yaffee

Administration and Production

Irene Baker
Amy Catlin
Amy Taber

**Cooperating Classrooms
for This Unit**

Barbara Fox
*Cambridge Public Schools
Cambridge, MA*

Alice Madio
*Winchester Public Schools
Winchester, MA*

Anne Scribner
*Shady Hill School
Cambridge, MA*

Technology Development

Douglas H. Clements
Julie Sarama

Video Production

David A. Smith
Judy Storeygard

Consultants and Advisors

Deborah Lowenberg Ball
Marilyn Burns
Mary Johnson
James J. Kaput
Mary M. Lindquist
Leslie P. Steffe
Grayson Wheatley

Graduate Assistants

Richard Aistrope
Kathryn Battista
Caroline Borrow
William Hunt
Kent State University

Jeffrey Barrett
Julie Sarama
Sudha Swaminathan
Elaine Vukelic
State University of New York at Buffalo

Dan Gillette
Irene Hall
Harvard Graduate School of Education

Revisions and Home Materials

Cathy Miles Grant
Marlene Kliman
Margaret McGaffigan
Megan Murray
Kim O'Neil
Andee Rubin
Susan Jo Russell
Lisa Seyferth
Myriam Steinback
Judy Storeygard
Anna Suarez
Cornelia Tierney
Carol Walker
Tracey Wright

CONTENTS

WHERE TO START

The first-time user of *Between Never and Always* should read the following:

When you next teach this same unit, you can begin to read more of the background. Each time you present the unit, you will learn more about how your students understand the mathematical ideas.

Investigations in Number, Data, and Space® is a K–5 mathematics curriculum with four major goals:

- to offer students meaningful mathematical problems
- to emphasize depth in mathematical thinking rather than superficial exposure to a series of fragmented topics
- to communicate mathematics content and pedagogy to teachers
- to substantially expand the pool of mathematically literate students

The *Investigations* curriculum embodies a new approach based on years of research about how children learn mathematics. Each grade level consists of a set of separate units, each offering 2–8 weeks of work. These units of study are presented through investigations that involve students in the exploration of major mathematical ideas.

Approaching the mathematics content through investigations helps students develop flexibility and confidence in approaching problems, fluency in using mathematical skills and tools to solve problems, and proficiency in evaluating their solutions. Students also build a repertoire of ways to communicate about their mathematical thinking, while their enjoyment and appreciation of mathematics grows.

The investigations are carefully designed to invite all students into mathematics—girls and boys, members of diverse cultural, ethnic, and language groups, and students with different strengths and interests. Problem contexts often call on students to share experiences from their family, culture, or community. The curriculum eliminates barriers—such as work in isolation from peers, or emphasis on speed and memorization—that exclude some students from participating successfully in mathematics. The following aspects of the curriculum ensure that all students are included in significant mathematics learning:

- Students spend time exploring problems in depth.
- They find more than one solution to many of the problems they work on.
- They invent their own strategies and approaches, rather than rely on memorized procedures.
- They choose from a variety of concrete materials and appropriate technology, including calculators, as a natural part of their everyday mathematical work.
- They express their mathematical thinking through drawing, writing, and talking.
- They work in a variety of groupings—as a whole class, individually, in pairs, and in small groups.
- They move around the classroom as they explore the mathematics in their environment and talk with their peers.

While reading and other language activities are typically given a great deal of time and emphasis in elementary classrooms, mathematics often does not get the time it needs. If students are to experience mathematics in depth, they must have enough time to become engaged in real mathematical problems. We believe that a minimum of 5 hours of mathematics classroom time a week—about an hour a day—is critical at the elementary level. The scope and pacing of the *Investigations* curriculum are based on that belief.

We explain more about the pedagogy and principles that underlie these investigations in Teacher Notes throughout the units. For correlations of the curriculum to the NCTM Standards and further help in using this research-based program for teaching mathematics, see the following books, available from Dale Seymour Publications:

- *Implementing the* Investigations in Number, Data, and Space® *Curriculum*
- *Beyond Arithmetic: Changing Mathematics in the Elementary Classroom* by Jan Mokros, Susan Jo Russell, and Karen Economopoulos

This book is one of the curriculum units for *Investigations in Number, Data, and Space.* In addition to providing part of a complete mathematics curriculum for your students, this unit offers information to support your own professional development. You, the teacher, are the person who will make this curriculum come alive in the classroom; the book for each unit is your main support system.

Although the curriculum does not include student textbooks, reproducible sheets for student work are provided in the unit and are also available as Student Activity Booklets. Students work actively with objects and experiences in their own environment and with a variety of manipulative materials and technology, rather than with a book of instruction and problems. We strongly recommend use of the overhead projector as a way to present problems, to focus group discussion, and to help students share ideas and strategies.

Ultimately, every teacher will use these investigations in ways that make sense for his or her particular style, the particular group of students, and the constraints and supports of a particular school environment. Each unit offers information and guidance for a wide variety of situations, drawn from our collaborations with many teachers and students over many years. Our goal in this book is to help you, a professional educator, implement this curriculum in a way that will give all your students access to mathematical power.

Investigation Format

The opening two pages of each investigation help you get ready for the work that follows.

What Happens This gives a synopsis of each session or block of sessions.

Mathematical Emphasis This lists the most important ideas and processes students will encounter in this investigation.

What to Plan Ahead of Time These lists alert you to materials to gather, sheets to duplicate, transparencies to make, and anything else you need to do before starting.

INVESTIGATION 2

Fair and Unfair Games

What Happens

Sessions 1 and 2: Rock, Paper, Scissors
Students play a three-person version of Rock, Paper, Scissors that is not fair—the players have different chances of winning. After collecting data that seem to show the game is unfair, students enumerate all possible ways for each player to win and discover that it is indeed unfair. Groups then modify the rules of the game to make it fair.

Session 3: Does a Fair Game Always Look Fair? Students make and share lists of games that involve chance only, skill only, and a combination of the two. They discuss any differences of opinion about how the games are classified. A new game, Race to the Top, is introduced; it is played with a one-half spinner that students know is fair. The class results are used to prompt a discussion of what it means for a game to be fair.

Sessions 4 and 5: The Unfair Spinner Game
Students report on the methods used by three different generations for deciding who goes first. They discuss the fairness of the various methods. Then, after playing a spinner game that is clearly unfair, groups modify the rules to make the game fair. After each group writes up rules for their game, students play the games designed by other groups and decide whether they agree that the games are fair.

Mathematical Emphasis

- Interpreting fairness of a game as equal probability of winning
- Developing systematic ways to generate a list that includes all the ways an event can occur
- Applying knowledge of probability to design a fair game
- Analyzing the fairness of games
- Distinguishing between games of chance and games of skill
- Interpreting data represented on line plots
- Analyzing group data in terms of general features such as center and spread
- Understanding variability in the results of fair games

What to Plan Ahead of Time

Materials

- Chart paper (Sessions 1–2 and 4–5)
- Clear spinners: 1 per pair (Sessions 3–5)
- One-half spinner templates from Investigation 1: 1 per pair (Session 3)
- Overhead projector (Sessions 3–5, optional)
- Pennies or other coins to flip: 1 per group (Sessions 4–5)

Other Preparation

- Duplicate student sheets and teaching resources (located at the end of this unit) in the following quantities. If you have Student Activity Booklets, copy only the item marked with an asterisk.

  For Sessions 1–2
  Student Sheet 9, Games of Skill and Chance (p. 91): 1 per student (homework)

  For Session 3
  Student Sheet 10, Race to the Top Score Sheet (p. 92): 1 per pair
  Student Sheet 11, Deciding Who Goes First (p. 93): 1 per student (homework)

  For Sessions 4–5
  Student Sheet 12, Assigning Household Jobs (p. 94): 1 per student (homework)
  Unfair Spinner Game Templates* (p. 95): 1 per group of 4, cut apart to make two spinners

- Make two demonstration spinners from the Unfair Spinner Game Templates (p. 95). (Sessions 4–5)

Sessions Within an investigation, the activities are organized by class session, a session being at least a one-hour math class. Sessions are numbered consecutively through an investigation. Often several sessions are grouped together, presenting a block of activities with a single major focus.

When you find a block of sessions presented together—for example, Sessions 1, 2, and 3—read through the entire block first to understand the overall flow and sequence of the activities. Make some preliminary decisions about how you will divide the activities into three sessions for your class, based on what you know about your students. You may need to modify your initial plans as you progress through the activities, and you may want to make notes in the margins of the pages as reminders for the next time you use the unit.

Be sure to read the Session Follow-Up section at the end of the session block to see what homework assignments and extensions are suggested as you make your initial plans.

While you may be used to a curriculum that tells you exactly what each class session should cover, we have found that the teacher is in a better position to make these decisions. Each unit is flexible and may be handled somewhat differently by every teacher. Although we provide guidance for how many sessions a particular group of activities is likely to need, we want you to be active in determining an appropriate pace and the best transition points for your class. It is not unusual for a teacher to spend more or less time than is proposed for the activities.

Ten-Minute Math At the beginning of some sessions, you will find Ten-Minute Math activities. These are designed to be used in tandem with the investigations, but not during the math hour. Rather, we hope you will do them whenever you have a spare 10 minutes—maybe before lunch or recess, or at the end of the day.

Ten-Minute Math offers practice in key concepts, but not always those being covered in the unit. For example, in a unit on using data, Ten-Minute Math might revisit geometric activities done earlier in the year. Complete directions for the suggested activities are included at the end of each unit.

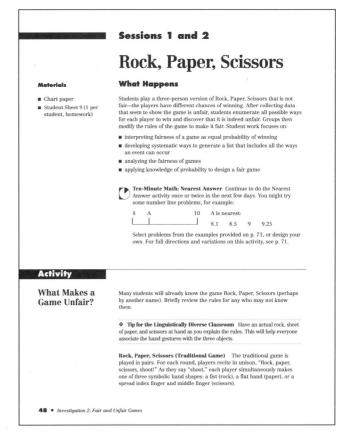

Sessions 1 and 2

Rock, Paper, Scissors

Materials

- Chart paper
- Student Sheet 9 (1 per student, homework)

What Happens

Students play a three-person version of Rock, Paper, Scissors that is not fair—the players have different chances of winning. After collecting data that seem to show the game is unfair, students enumerate all possible ways for each player to win and discover that it is indeed unfair. Groups then modify the rules of the game to make it fair. Student work focuses on:

- interpreting fairness of a game as equal probability of winning
- developing systematic ways to generate a list that includes all the ways an event can occur
- analyzing the fairness of games
- applying knowledge of probability to design a fair game

Ten-Minute Math: Nearest Answer Continue to do the Nearest Answer activity once or twice in the next few days. You might try some number line problems, for example:

8   A   10   A is nearest:
                                8.1   8.5   9   9.25

Select problems from the examples provided on p. 71, or design your own. For full directions and variations on this activity, see p. 71.

Activity

What Makes a Game Unfair?

Many students will already know the game Rock, Paper, Scissors (perhaps by another name). Briefly review the rules for any who may not know them.

❖ **Tip for the Linguistically Diverse Classroom** Have an actual rock, sheet of paper, and scissors at hand as you explain the rules. This will help everyone associate the hand gestures with the three objects.

Rock, Paper, Scissors (Traditional Game) The traditional game is played in pairs. For each round, players recite in unison, "Rock, paper, scissors, shoot!" As they say "shoot," each player simultaneously makes one of three symbolic hand shapes: a fist (rock), a flat hand (paper), or a spread index finger and middle finger (scissors).

48 ■ *Investigation 2: Fair and Unfair Games*

Activities The activities include pair and small-group work, individual tasks, and whole-class discussions. In any case, students are seated together, talking and sharing ideas during all work times. Students most often work cooperatively, although each student may record work individually.

Choice Time In some units, some sessions are structured with activity choices. In these cases, students may work simultaneously on different activities focused on the same mathematical ideas. Students choose which activities they want to do, and they cycle through them.

You will need to decide how to set up and introduce these activities and how to let students make their choices. Some teachers present them as station activities, in different parts of the room. Some list the choices on the board as reminders or have students keep their own lists.

Tips for the Linguistically Diverse Classroom At strategic points in each unit, you will find concrete suggestions for simple modifications of the teaching strategies to encourage the participation of all students. Many of these tips offer alternative ways to elicit critical thinking from students at varying levels of English proficiency, as well as from other students who find it difficult to verbalize their thinking.

The tips are supported by suggestions for specific vocabulary work to help ensure that all students can participate fully in the investigations. The Preview for the Linguistically Diverse Classroom lists important words that are assumed as part of the working vocabulary of the unit. Second-language learners will need to become familiar with these words in order to understand the problems and activities they will be doing. These terms can be incorporated into students' second-language work before or during the unit. Activities that can be used to present the words are found in the appendix, Vocabulary Support for Second-Language Learners. In addition, ideas for making connections to students' languages and cultures, included on the Preview page, help the class explore the unit's concepts from a multicultural perspective.

Session Follow-Up: Homework In *Investigations,* homework is an extension of classroom work. Sometimes it offers review and practice of work done in class, sometimes preparation for upcoming activities, and sometimes numerical practice that revisits work in earlier units. Homework plays a role both in supporting students' learning and in helping inform families about the ways in which students in this curriculum work with mathematical ideas.

Depending on your school's homework policies and your own judgment, you may want to assign more homework than is suggested in the units. For this purpose you might use the practice pages, included as blackline masters at the end of this unit, to give students additional work with numbers.

For some homework assignments, you will want to adapt the activity to meet the needs of a variety of students in your class: those with special needs, those ready for more challenge, and second-language learners. You might change the numbers in a problem, make the activity more or less complex, or go through a sample activity with

those who need extra help. You can modify any student sheet for either homework or class use. In particular, making numbers in a problem smaller or larger can make the same basic activity appropriate for a wider range of students.

Another issue to consider is how to handle the homework that students bring back to class—how to recognize the work they have done at home without spending too much time on it. Some teachers hold a short group discussion of different approaches to the assignment; others ask students to share and discuss their work with a neighbor; still others post the homework around the room and give students time to tour it briefly. If you want to keep track of homework students bring in, be sure it ends up in a designated place.

Session Follow-Up: Extensions Sometimes in Session Follow-Up, you will find suggested extension activities. These are opportunities for some or all students to explore a topic in greater depth or in a different context. They are not designed for "fast" students; mathematics is a multifaceted discipline, and different students will want to go further in different investigations. Look for and encourage the sparks of interest and enthusiasm you see in your students, and use the extensions to help them pursue these interests.

Excursions   Some of the *Investigations* units include excursions—blocks of activities that could be omitted without harming the integrity of the unit. This is one way of dealing with the great depth and variety of elementary mathematics— much more than a class has time to explore in any one year. Excursions give you the flexibility to make different choices from year to year, doing the excursion in one unit this time, and next year trying another excursion.

Materials

A complete list of the materials needed for teaching this unit follows the unit overview. Some of these materials are available in kits for the *Investigations* curriculum. Individual items can also be purchased from school supply dealers.

Classroom Materials   In an active mathematics classroom, certain basic materials should be available at all times: interlocking cubes, pencils, unlined paper, graph paper, calculators, things to count with, and measuring tools. Some activities in this curriculum require scissors and glue sticks or tape. Stick-on notes and large paper are also useful materials throughout.

So that students can independently get what they need at any time, they should know where these materials are kept, how they are stored, and how they are to be returned to the storage area. For example, interlocking cubes are best stored in towers of ten; then, whatever the activity, they should be returned to storage in groups of ten at the end of the hour. You'll find that establishing such routines at the beginning of the year is well worth the time and effort.

Student Sheets and Teaching Resources   Student recording sheets and other teaching tools needed for both class and homework are provided as reproducible blackline masters at the end of each unit. We think it's important that students find their own ways of organizing and recording their work. They need to learn how to explain their thinking with both drawings and written words, and how to organize their results so someone else can understand them. For this reason, we deliberately do not provide student sheets for every activity. Regardless of the form in which students do their work, we recommend that they keep their

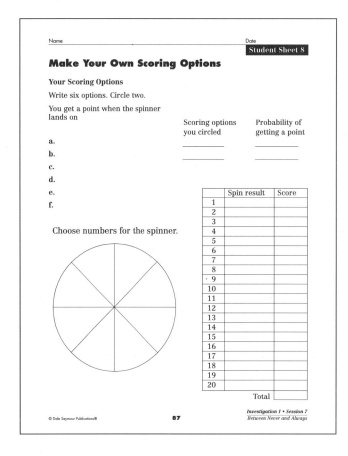

work in a mathematics folder, journal, or notebook so that it is always available to them for reference.

Student Activity Booklets   These booklets contain all the sheets each student will need for individual work, freeing you from extensive copying (although you may need or want to copy the occasional teaching resource on transparency film or card stock, or make extra copies of a student sheet).

Calculators and Computers   Calculators are used throughout *Investigations*. Many of the units recommend that you have at least one calculator for each pair. You will find calculator activities, plus Teacher Notes discussing this important mathematical tool, in an early unit at each grade level. It is assumed that calculators will be readily available for student use.

Computer activities are offered at all grade levels. How you use the computer activities depends on the number of computers you have available. Technology in the Curriculum discusses ways to incorporate the use of calculators and computers into classroom activities.

Children's Literature   Each unit offers a list of related children's literature that can be used to support the mathematical ideas in the unit. Sometimes an activity is based on a specific children's book, with suggestions for substitutions where practical. While such activities can be adapted and taught without the book, the literature offers a rich introduction and should be used whenever possible.

Investigations at Home   It is a good idea to make your policy on homework explicit to both students and their families when you begin teaching with *Investigations*. How frequently will you be assigning homework? When do you expect homework to be completed and brought back to school? What are your goals in assigning homework? How independent should families expect their children to be? What should the parent's or guardian's role be? The more explicit you can be about your expectations, the better the homework experience will be for everyone.

Investigations at Home (a booklet available separately for each unit, to send home with students) gives you a way to communicate with families about the work students are doing in class. This booklet includes a brief description of every session, a list of the mathematics content emphasized in each investigation, and a discussion of each homework assignment to help families more effectively support their children. Whether or not you are using the *Investigations* at Home booklets, we expect you to make your own choices about homework assignments. Feel free to omit any and to add extra ones you think are appropriate.

Family Letter   A letter that you can send home to students' families is included with the blackline masters for each unit. Families need to be informed about the mathematics work in your classroom; they should be encouraged to participate in and support their children's work. A reminder to send home the letter for each unit appears in one of the early investigations. These letters are also available separately in Spanish, Vietnamese, Cantonese, Hmong, and Cambodian.

Help for You, the Teacher

Because we believe strongly that a new curriculum must help teachers think in new ways about mathematics and about their students' mathematical thinking processes, we have included a great deal of material to help you learn more about both.

About the Mathematics in This Unit   This introductory section summarizes the critical information about the mathematics you will be teaching. It describes the unit's central mathematical ideas and the ways students will encounter them through the unit's activities.

About the Assessment in This Unit   This introductory section highlights Teacher Checkpoints and assessment activities contained in the unit. It offers questions to stimulate your assessment as you observe the development of students' mathematical thinking and learning.

Teacher Notes   These reference notes provide practical information about the mathematics you are teaching and about our experience with how students learn. Many of the notes were written in response to actual questions from teachers or to discuss important things we saw happening in the

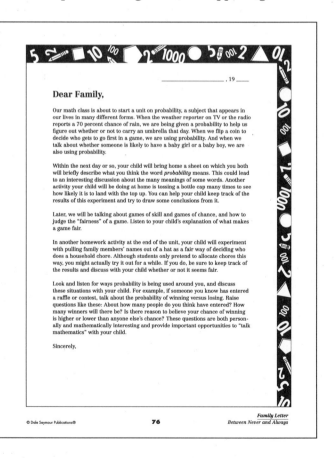

field-test classrooms. Some teachers like to read them all before starting the unit, then review them as they come up in particular investigations.

Dialogue Boxes Sample dialogues demonstrate how students typically express their mathematical ideas, what issues and confusions arise in their thinking, and how some teachers have guided class discussions.

These dialogues are based on the extensive classroom testing of this curriculum; many are word-for-word transcriptions of recorded class discussions. They are not always easy reading; sometimes it may take some effort to unravel what the students are trying to say. But this is the value of these dialogues; they offer good clues to how your students may develop and express their approaches and strategies, helping you prepare for your own class discussions.

Where to Start You may not have time to read everything the first time you use this unit. As a first-time user, you will likely focus on understanding the activities and working them out with your students. Read completely through all the activities before starting to present them. Also read those sections listed in the Contents under the heading Where to Start.

Teacher Note ▷ *What's Different About This Unit?*

If you have studied probability before, you may be surprised by the focus of this two-week unit.

Probability is often introduced with coins and number cubes, determining how many ways there are for various events to occur. The probability of rolling a 5 with a fair number cube, for example, is ⅙ because it is one of six equally likely numbers you could roll. The probability of rolling an odd number is ³⁄₆ or ½ because, of the six equally likely events, three of them (1, 3, 5) are odd numbers. This way of talking about probability is referred to as *theoretical* probability, because it describes what would happen "in theory" when a number cube is rolled.

However, probability in our lives does not work exactly as it does "in theory." If we actually roll a number cube ten times, we *may* get an odd number exactly half of the time (5 times)—but we may get an odd number only 4 times out of 10 or we may get an odd number 6 times out of 10. This way of talking about probability is referred to as *experimental* probability because it describes what happens when we do an experiment such as rolling a number cube 10 times.

Perhaps the most important concept of this unit is understanding the difference between theoretical and experimental probability. Many of the activities in this unit involve repeating chance events (such as flipping a coin or rolling a number cube) many times. Through these probability experiments, students will be able to see that their results are usually not exactly what they expect according to theoretical probability and that they seldom get identical results when they repeat an experiment.

The experiments students conduct will lead to some questions that get to the heart of the difference between theoretical and experimental probability, e.g., If a coin has a ½ chance of turning up heads on a single flip, why doesn't it turn up heads exactly half of the time? For more help in discussing this distinction with your students, see the **Teacher Note**, Why Doesn't a Half-Green Spinner Spin Green Half the Time? (p. 24).

We all deal with uncertainty in our lives every day, so both you and your students have probably developed everyday intuitions about chance events. Unfortunately, some of the informal, intuitive ideas we form about probability are not in agreement with the mathematics of probability. Be aware of this potential clash—for both you and your students—and realize that it may make learning probability a bit more difficult than other mathematical topics.

You might notice that the unit doesn't include many probabilities of real-world events. This is partly because we want students to discover the meaning of probability through events they can experiment with in the classroom. It's also the case that many of the events important to us have very small probabilities, and developing appropriate intuitions about the meaning of probability with values such as 1 in a million is considerably more difficult than with values such as 1 in 2 or 1 in 4.

Nonetheless, you can link this study of probability to real-world events as suggested in the extension on p. 13. Look for opportunities to introduce a probability associated with a current event that students are aware of, have them locate it on the likelihood line, and discuss what they think the probability value means in that particular situation.

Don't expect your students to understand all the implications of the ideas in this unit. We consider this to be one of several opportunities your students will have to work with probability in their studies of mathematics. The Teacher Notes in the unit highlight the important ideas that you should focus on in your class discussions and in your explorations of probability.

D I A L O G U E   B O X

Discussing Spinner Results

This class is discussing the results pairs got from spinning the half-green spinner 50 times (p. 17).

```
            X   X X
 X        X X X X X X                              X
 19 20 21 22 23 24 25 26 27 28 29 30 31 32 33 34 35
```

How do our results compare to what we expected?

Noah: Most of us got 23, 25, or 26. And that's about what we predicted.

Cara: Except for the 35.

Noah: No, but remember, we said that it wouldn't work out exactly 25 for everyone, and it didn't. So, we did get what we expected.

Cara, are you saying that the 35 surprised you? And how about the 19?

Cara: The 19 seems like it wouldn't be that hard to get, but the 35 is way, way out there—really far from the rest of the scores, from the 25.

Mei-Ling: When we got it, we thought something was wrong with our spinner, but we did it again and got 23 the second time.

Are there any other ways to explain the 35?

Leon: Maybe whoever was spinning, they weren't spinning hard enough.

Natalie: Or maybe they counted wrong.

Tai: I was keeping track, and I know it was 35.

Any other possible ways to explain the 35? *[long pause]* **What do you think the probability is of getting a 35 if the spinner and everything else is working as it should? That is, what's the probability of it just happening because of chance?**

Natalie: Pretty low.

Manuel: Yeah, but it could happen. And maybe this was one of those times.

Did anything else surprise you?

Matt: Yeah. I didn't think anyone would spin exactly one-half. When Katrina got exactly 25, I was really surprised.

Why?

Matt: 'Cause I thought there was very little chance of getting exactly what you expect. Things hardly ever work out perfectly.

Trevor: Well, but it's not like the spinner is thinking, "Don't come out exactly even," so 25 should be as likely as any other result.

Do you think, Trevor, that 25 is *more* likely than other results?

Trevor: Well, more likely than say 30, or 20, but maybe not much different than other scores right around 25.

Can someone summarize what we found, referring to our line plot?

Jasmine: You don't always get the same thing.

Can you say that and refer to our results?

Jasmine: We got results all the way from 19 to 35, but most of them were pretty close to 25.

Zach: The results are spread out, but most are in the middle.

Shakita: Most of the scores are close to 25, and that's one-half. That's what we predicted.

The teacher picked up on Cara's mention of the outlier 35 to help students see that they need not account for such scores by questioning the fairness of the spinner. It is fairly typical to get a few scores out at the extremes when we conduct a chance experiment many times.

The teacher then helped the students attend to more general features of the results. This is important, because many students tend to focus on a single feature of the data, such as one score that seems especially far out, or the clump in the center. When students are encouraged to share what they see, they can begin to develop their ability to see multiple features.

The *Investigations* curriculum incorporates the use of two forms of technology in the classroom: calculators and computers. Calculators are assumed to be standard classroom materials, available for student use in any unit. Computers are explicitly linked to one or more units at each grade level; they are used with the unit on 2-D geometry at each grade, as well as with some of the units on measuring, data, and changes.

Using Calculators

In this curriculum, calculators are considered tools for doing mathematics, similar to pattern blocks or interlocking cubes. Just as with other tools, students must learn both *how* to use calculators correctly and *when* they are appropriate to use. This knowledge is crucial for daily life, as calculators are now a standard way of handling numerical operations, both at work and at home.

Using a calculator correctly is not a simple task; it depends on a good knowledge of the four operations and of the number system, so that students can select suitable calculations and also determine what a reasonable result would be. These skills are the basis of any work with numbers, whether or not a calculator is involved.

Unfortunately, calculators are often seen as tools to check computations with, as if other methods are somehow more fallible. Students need to understand that any computational method can be used to check any other; it's just as easy to make a mistake on the calculator as it is to make a mistake on paper or with mental arithmetic. Throughout this curriculum, we encourage students to solve computation problems in more than one way in order to double-check their accuracy. We present mental arithmetic, paper-and-pencil computation, and calculators as three possible approaches.

In this curriculum we also recognize that, despite their importance, calculators are not always appropriate in mathematics instruction. Like any tools, calculators are useful for some tasks but not for others. You will need to make decisions about when to allow students access to calculators and when to ask that they solve problems without them so that they can concentrate on other tools and skills. At times when calculators are or are not appropriate for a particular activity, we make specific recommendations. Help your students develop their own sense of which problems they can tackle with their own reasoning and which ones might be better solved with a combination of their own reasoning and the calculator.

Managing calculators in your classroom so that they are a tool, and not a distraction, requires some planning. When calculators are first introduced, students often want to use them for everything, even problems that can be solved quite simply by other methods. However, once the novelty wears off, students are just as interested in developing their own strategies, especially when these strategies are emphasized and valued in the classroom. Over time, students will come to recognize the ease and value of solving problems mentally, with paper and pencil, or with manipulatives, while also understanding the power of the calculator to facilitate work with larger numbers.

Experience shows that if calculators are available only occasionally, students become excited and distracted when they are permitted to use them. They focus on the tool rather than on the mathematics. In order to learn when calculators are appropriate and when they are not, students must have easy access to them and use them routinely in their work.

If you have a calculator for each student, and if you think your students can accept the responsibility, you might allow them to keep their calculators with the rest of their individual materials, at least for the first few weeks of school. Alternatively, you might store them in boxes on a shelf, number each calculator, and assign a corresponding number to each student. This system can give students a sense of ownership while also helping you keep track of the calculators.

Using Computers

Students can use computers to approach and visualize mathematical situations in new ways. The computer allows students to construct and manipulate geometric shapes, see objects move according to rules they specify, and turn, flip, and repeat a pattern.

This curriculum calls for computers in units where they are a particularly effective tool for learning mathematics content. One unit on 2-D geometry at each of the grades 3–5 includes a core of activities that rely on access to computers, either in the classroom or in a lab. Other units on geometry, measuring, data, and changes include computer activities, but can be taught without them. In these units, however, students' experience is greatly enhanced by computer use.

The following list outlines the recommended use of computers in this curriculum:

Kindergarten
Unit: *Making Shapes and Building Blocks*
   (Exploring Geometry)
Software: *Shapes*
Source: provided with the unit

Grade 1
Unit: *Survey Questions and Secret Rules*
   (Collecting and Sorting Data)
Software: *Tabletop, Jr.*
Source: Broderbund

Unit: *Quilt Squares and Block Towns*
   (2-D and 3-D Geometry)
Software: *Shapes*
Source: provided with the unit

Grade 2
Unit: *Mathematical Thinking at Grade 2*
   (Introduction)
Software: *Shapes*
Source: provided with the unit

Unit: *Shapes, Halves, and Symmetry*
   (Geometry and Fractions)
Software: *Shapes*
Source: provided with the unit

Unit: *How Long? How Far?* (Measuring)
Software: *Geo-Logo*
Source: provided with the unit

Grade 3
Unit: *Flips, Turns, and Area* (2-D Geometry)
Software: *Tumbling Tetrominoes*
Source: provided with the unit

Unit: *Turtle Paths* (2-D Geometry)
Software: *Geo-Logo*
Source: provided with the unit

Grade 4
Unit: *Sunken Ships and Grid Patterns*
   (2-D Geometry)
Software: *Geo-Logo*
Source: provided with the unit

Grade 5
Unit: *Picturing Polygons* (2-D Geometry)
Software: *Geo-Logo*
Source: provided with the unit

Unit: *Patterns of Change* (Tables and Graphs)
Software: *Trips*
Source: provided with the unit

Unit: *Data: Kids, Cats, and Ads* (Statistics)
Software: *Tabletop, Sr.*
Source: Broderbund

The software provided with the *Investigations* units uses the power of the computer to help students explore mathematical ideas and relationships that cannot be explored in the same way with physical materials. With the *Shapes* (grades 1–2) and *Tumbling Tetrominoes* (grade 3) software, students explore symmetry, pattern, rotation and reflection, area, and characteristics of 2-D shapes. With the *Geo-Logo* software (grades 2–5), students investigate rotations and reflections, coordinate geometry, the properties of 2-D shapes, and angles. The *Trips* software (grade 5) is a mathematical exploration of motion in which students run experiments and interpret data presented in graphs and tables.

We suggest that students work in pairs on the computer; this not only maximizes computer resources but also encourages students to consult, monitor, and teach each other. Generally, more than two students at one computer find it difficult to share. Managing access to computers is an issue for every classroom. The curriculum gives you explicit support for setting up a system. The units are structured on the assumption that you have enough computers for half your students to work on the machines in pairs at one time. If you do not have access to that many computers, suggestions are made for structuring class time to use the unit with fewer than five.

Assessment plays a critical role in teaching and learning, and it is an integral part of the *Investigations* curriculum. For a teacher using these units, assessment is an ongoing process. You observe students' discussions and explanations of their strategies on a daily basis and examine their work as it evolves. While students are busy recording and representing their work, working on projects, sharing with partners, and playing mathematical games, you have many opportunities to observe their mathematical thinking. What you learn through observation guides your decisions about how to proceed. In any of the units, you will repeatedly consider questions like these:

- Do students come up with their own strategies for solving problems, or do they expect others to tell them what to do? What do their strategies reveal about their mathematical understanding?
- Do students understand that there are different strategies for solving problems? Do they articulate their strategies and try to understand other students' strategies?
- How effectively do students use materials as tools to help with their mathematical work?
- Do students have effective ideas for keeping track of and recording their work? Do keeping track of and recording their work seem difficult for them?

You will need to develop a comfortable and efficient system for recording and keeping track of your observations. Some teachers keep a clipboard handy and jot notes on a class list or on adhesive labels that are later transferred to student files. Others keep loose-leaf notebooks with a page for each student and make weekly notes about what they have observed in class.

Assessment Tools in the Unit

With the activities in each unit, you will find questions to guide your thinking while observing the students at work. You will also find two built-in assessment tools: Teacher Checkpoints and embedded Assessment activities.

Teacher Checkpoints The designated Teacher Checkpoints in each unit offer a time to "check in" with individual students, watch them at work, and ask questions that illuminate how they are thinking.

At first it may be hard to know what to look for, hard to know what kinds of questions to ask. Students may be reluctant to talk; they may not be accustomed to having the teacher ask them about their work, or they may not know how to explain their thinking. Two important ingredients of this process are asking students open-ended questions about their work and showing genuine interest in how they are approaching the task. When students see that you are interested in their thinking and are counting on them to come up with their own ways of solving problems, they may surprise you with the depth of their understanding.

Teacher Checkpoints also give you the chance to pause in the teaching sequence and reflect on how your class is doing overall. Think about whether you need to adjust your pacing: Are most students fluent with strategies for solving a particular kind of problem? Are they just starting to formulate good strategies? Or are they still struggling with how to start? Depending on what you see as the students work, you may want to spend more time on similar problems, change some of the problems to use smaller numbers, move quickly to more-challenging material, modify subsequent activities for some students, work on particular ideas with a small group, or pair students who have good strategies with those who are having more difficulty.

Embedded Assessment Activities Assessment activities embedded in each unit will help you examine specific pieces of student work, figure out what they mean, and provide feedback. From the students' point of view, these assessment activities are no different from any others. Each is a learning experience in and of itself, as well as an opportunity for you to gather evidence about students' mathematical understanding.

The embedded assessment activities sometimes involve writing and reflecting; at other times, a discussion or brief interaction between student and teacher; and in still other instances, the creation and explanation of a product. In most cases, the assessments require that students *show* what they did, *write* or *talk* about it, or do both. Having to explain how they worked through a problem helps students be more focused and clear in their mathematical thinking. It also helps them realize that doing mathematics is a process that may involve tentative starts, revising one's approach, taking different paths, and working through ideas.

Teachers often find the hardest part of assessment to be interpreting their students' work. We provide guidelines to help with that interpretation. If you have used a process approach to teaching writing, the assessment in *Investigations* will seem familiar. For many of the assessment activities, a Teacher Note provides examples of student work and a commentary on what it indicates about student thinking.

Documentation of Student Growth

To form an overall picture of mathematical progress, it is important to document each student's work. Many teachers have students keep their work in folders, notebooks, or journals, and some like to have students summarize their learning in journals at the end of each unit. It's important to document students' progress, and we recommend that you keep a portfolio of selected work for each student, unit by unit, for the entire year. The final activity in each *Investigations* unit, called Choosing Student Work to Save, helps you and the students select representative samples for a record of their work.

This kind of regular documentation helps you synthesize information about each student as a mathematical learner. From different pieces of evidence, you can put together the big picture. This synthesis will be invaluable in thinking about where to go next with a particular child, deciding where more work is needed, or explaining to parents (or other teachers) how a child is doing.

If you use portfolios, you need to collect a good balance of work, yet avoid being swamped with an overwhelming amount of paper. Following are some tips for effective portfolios:

- Collect a representative sample of work, including some pieces that students themselves select for inclusion in the portfolio. There should be just a few pieces for each unit, showing different kinds of work—some assignments that involve writing as well as some that do not.

- If students do not date their work, do so yourself so that you can reconstruct the order in which pieces were done.

- Include your reflections on the work. When you are looking back over the whole year, such comments are reminders of what seemed especially interesting about a particular piece; they can also be helpful to other teachers and to parents. Older students should be encouraged to write their own reflections about their work.

Assessment Overview

There are two places to turn for a preview of the assessment opportunities in each *Investigations* unit. The Assessment Resources column in the unit Overview Chart identifies the Teacher Checkpoints and Assessment activities embedded in each investigation, guidelines for observing the students that appear within classroom activities, and any Teacher Notes and Dialogue Boxes that explain what to look for and what types of student responses you might expect to see in your classroom. Additionally, the section About the Assessment in This Unit gives you a detailed list of questions for each investigation, keyed to the mathematical emphases, to help you observe student growth.

Depending on your situation, you may want to provide additional assessment opportunities. Most of the investigations lend themselves to more frequent assessment, simply by having students do more writing and recording while they are working.

Between Never and Always

Content of This Unit Students develop a likelihood line on which they locate the probability of various events occurring. As reference points on the line, they first use words (such as *impossible, uncertain, certain*) and later the numbers 0, 1, and simple fractions. Students learn to interpret a probability as a statement of how often a repeatable event will happen, rather than as a predictor of whether or not the event will happen on a particular occasion. They explore a variety of spinners, predicting what will happen if they spin each one 50 times, and comparing their predictions with the actual results obtained by students in the class. They apply this knowledge in testing their own guessing skills. They also investigate the fairness of a number of games, such as Rock, Paper, Scissors, and, if they are not fair, suggest modifications to make them so.

Connections with Other Units If you are doing the full-year *Investigations* curriculum in the suggested sequence for grade 5, this is the fourth of nine units. It assumes some experience with fractions, decimals, and percents, as presented in the grade 5 unit *Name That Portion*. In their analysis of the data they are collecting, students build on skills introduced in the grade 4 unit, *The Shape of the Data;* these skills will be extended in the grade 5 Statistics unit *Data: Kids, Cats, and Ads*.

This unit can also be used successfully at grade 6, depending on the previous experience and needs of your students.

Investigations Curriculum ■ Suggested Grade 5 Sequence

Mathematical Thinking at Grade 5 (Introduction and Landmarks in the Number System)

Picturing Polygons (2-D Geometry)

Name That Portion (Fractions, Percents, and Decimals)

▶ *Between Never and Always* (Probability)

Building on Numbers You Know (Computation and Estimation Strategies)

Measurement Benchmarks (Estimating and Measuring)

Patterns of Change (Tables and Graphs)

Containers and Cubes (3-D Geometry: Volume)

Data: Kids, Cats, and Ads (Statistics)

Investigation 1 ▪ Finding and Comparing Probabilities

Class Sessions	Activities	Pacing
Sessions 1 and 2 (p. 4) CREATING A LIKELIHOOD LINE	Setting Up a Likelihood Line Placing Events on the Likelihood Line Discussing Different Points of View Using Fractions as Measures of Probability Teacher Checkpoint: Placing Probabilities Homework: Creating a Likelihood Line Homework: What Is Probability? Extension: Probability and Real-World Risks	minimum 2 hr
Sessions 3 and 4 (p. 16) USING SPINNERS	What We Mean by Probability Spinning a One-Half Spinner One-Fourth and Three-Fourths Spinners Discussing the Spinner Results Homework: Bottle Cap Toss Extension: Collecting Data on Several in a Row	minimum 2 hr
Session 5 (p. 27) TESTING GUESSING SKILLS	Organizing the Bottle Cap Data Testing for Special Guessing Skills Extension: Matching Spinners	minimum 1 hr
Session 6 (p. 33) GUESSING SKILLS DISTRIBUTIONS	Looking at the Guessing Skills Results Judging Results: Likely or Unlikely? Extension: Retesting High Scorers	minimum 1 hr
Session 7 (p. 40) THE SCORING OPTIONS GAME	Learning the Game Strategy Playing the Scoring Options Game How Did We Get the Highest Scores? Homework: Make Your Own Scoring Options	minimum 1 hr

◐ **Ten-Minute Math** ▪ **Nearest Answer**

Mathematical Emphasis

- Associating verbal descriptions with numeric descriptions of probability and understanding the meaning of the word *probability*

- Seeing that repeating a probability experiment several times yields a variety of results

- Using a probability to predict about how often an event will happen in a given number of trials

- Estimating probabilities from results of actual trials

- Predicting and analyzing features of distributions

- Learning to add probabilities of simple events

Assessment Resources

Teacher Checkpoint: Placing Probabilities (p. 11)

Impossible, Certain, and Everything in Between (Teacher Note, p. 15)

Materials

Clear, unmarked spinners

Overhead projector, pens, and transparencies

Stick-on notes

Large paper

Envelopes

Butcher paper or accordion-fold printer paper

Green markers or crayons

Bottle caps

Family letter

Student Sheets 1–8

Teaching resource sheets

Investigation 2 ▪ Fair and Unfair Games

Class Sessions	Activities	Pacing
Sessions 1 and 2 (p. 48) ROCK, PAPER, SCISSORS	What Makes a Game Unfair? Making the Game Fair Playing New Versions of the Game Homework: Games of Skill and Chance	minimum 2 hr
Session 3 (p. 58) DOES A FAIR GAME ALWAYS LOOK FAIR?	Games of Skill, Games of Chance A Fair Game: Race to the Top Class Results from Race to the Top Homework: Deciding Who Goes First Extension: Making Line Plots of Their Own Results Extension: Playing a Game from a Different Culture	minimum 1 hr
Sessions 4 and 5 (p. 64) THE UNFAIR SPINNER GAME	Who Goes First: What's Fair? Playing the Unfair Spinner Game Designing a Fair Game with Unfair Spinners Assessment: Judging the Fairness of Games Choosing Student Work to Save Homework: Assigning Household Jobs Extension: Discussing the Household Jobs Homework	minimum 2 hr

🕐 **Ten-Minute Math ▪ Nearest Answer**

Mathematical Emphasis

- Interpreting fairness of a game as equal probability of winning

- Developing systematic ways to generate a list that includes all the ways an event can occur

- Applying knowledge of probability to design a fair game, and analyzing the fairness of games (and interpreting fairness of a game as equal probability of winning)

- Distinguishing between games of chance and games of skill

- Interpreting and analyzing group data represented on line plots

- Understanding variability in the results of fair games

Assessment Resources

What's Fair? (Teacher Note, p. 55)

Discussing Students' New Game Rules (Dialogue Box, p. 56)

What to Expect from the Fair Version of Race to the Top (Teacher Note, p. 62)

Bad Breaks in Fair Games (Dialogue Box, p. 63)

Assessment: Judging the Fairness of Games (p. 68)

Choosing Student Work to Save (p. 69)

Materials

Chart paper
Clear spinners
Overhead projector
Coins
Student Sheets 9–12
Teaching resource sheets

Following are the basic materials needed for the activities in this unit. Many of the items can be purchased from the publisher, either individually or in the Teacher Resource Package and the Student Materials Kit for grade 5. Detailed information is available on the *Investigations* order form. To obtain this form, call toll-free 1-800-872-1100 and ask for a Dale Seymour customer service representative.

Clear, unmarked spinners (1 per pair)

Butcher paper or accordion-fold printer paper (need about 17 feet altogether; may substitute letter-size sheets taped together)

Pennies or other coins to flip (1 per group)

Chart paper

Stick-on notes (3-inch size; at least 10 per group)

Large paper, 12" by 18" (1 sheet per group)

Envelopes (1 per group)

Bottle caps (1 per student, homework; they may supply their own unless you want students to have the same kind)

Green markers or crayons

Overhead projector, pens, and transparencies

The following materials are provided at the end of this unit as blackline masters. A Student Activity Booklet containing all student sheets and teaching resources needed for individual work is available.

Family Letter (p. 76)

Student Sheets 1–12 (p. 77)

Teaching Resources:

    Spinner Templates (one-half, one-fourth, three-fourths) (p. 88)

    Guessing Skills Spinner Templates (p. 90)

    Unfair Spinner Game Templates (p. 95)

Practice Pages (p. 97)

Related Children's Literature

Van Allsburg, Chris. *Jumanji*. Boston: Houghton-Mifflin, 1981.

Most of the decisions we make every day are based on partial or uncertain information. We decide to go ahead with the picnic we planned even though the weather report says there's a chance of rain. We give ourselves 10 minutes to get to school even though some unusual circumstances could make us late. There's really no alternative to making these types of decisions. We would never go on a picnic if we waited for a day when there was zero chance of rain, nor could we leave early enough to guarantee our timely arrival at school given every possible circumstance that could delay us.

Being able to think probabilistically is important to us, and not only in making everyday decisions. Probability allows pollsters to figure out how big a sample we need to predict the outcome of an election; it allows medical researchers to test the effectiveness of a new treatment for cancer. Probability is also an important part of many areas of study, including physics, economics, and biology. This unit introduces students to a few fundamental ideas about probability. They will learn to

- associate verbal descriptions of probability with numeric descriptions

- interpret a probability as a measure of how often an event will occur

- describe distributions in terms of their shape and where the data are centered

- use proportional reasoning to estimate how often a probabilistic event will occur in some number of trials

- apply knowledge of probability to design a fair game

Two major ideas are stressed throughout this unit. The first is that the probability of an event tells us how often to expect that event to occur over many repetitions. For example, the probability of rolling a five with a fair die is $\frac{1}{6}$. Thus we expect that if we roll a die many times, roughly $\frac{1}{6}$ of the rolls will be five.

The second major idea is that when we actually conduct trials with objects like dice, the results vary considerably. For example, if a large number of students rolled a die 60 times and recorded how many fives they got, we would see that many of them would get around 10 fives, which is what we would expect based on probability (10 is $\frac{1}{6}$ of 60). However, most of the students would not get exactly 10 fives. The results would be spread out over a range, with some students getting as many as 16 or 17 fives or as few as 3 or 4 fives.

Thus, probability does not allow us to predict what will happen next, or even exactly what we will get if we roll the die many times. But probability does tell us something about what to expect in large samples. For example, we know that the median of all the students' results of rolling the die 60 times will be very close to 10.

In our own lives, probability cannot guarantee that we will make correct decisions. Rather, it helps us make decisions that, in the long run, will turn out better on average than if we didn't use probabilistic thinking. And it also helps us understand that very unusual events will occasionally happen just by chance.

At the beginning of each investigation, the Mathematical Emphasis section tells you what is most important for students to learn about during that investigation. Many of these understandings and processes are difficult and complex. Students gradually learn more and more about each idea over many years of schooling. Individual students will begin and end the unit with different levels of knowledge and skill, but all will gain knowledge of how we figure out probabilities of uncertain events and of what these probabilities do and don't allow us to predict about future occurrences.

Throughout the *Investigations* curriculum, there are many opportunities for ongoing daily assessment as you observe, listen to, and interact with students at work. In this unit, you will find one Teacher Checkpoint:

> Investigation 1, Sessions 1–2:
> Placing Probabilities (p. 11)

This unit also has one embedded assessment activity:

> Investigation 2, Sessions 4–5:
> Judging the Fairness of Games (p. 68)

In addition, you can use almost any activity in this unit to assess your students' needs and strengths. Listed below are questions to help you focus your observation in each investigation. You may want to keep track of your observations for each student to help you plan your curriculum and monitor students' growth. Suggestions for documenting student growth can be found in the section About Assessment.

Investigation 1: Finding and Comparing Probabilities

■ In what ways do students associate verbal descriptions with numeric descriptions of probability? Do they have an understanding of *probability* as determining how likely something is to occur?

■ What do students expect will result from repeating a probability experiment? Do they expect it to yield a variety of results? What reasoning do they use to predict about how often an event will happen in a given number of trials?

■ What strategies do students use for estimating probabilities from results of actual trials?

■ How do students go about predicting and analyzing features of distributions? How do they use characteristic features such as center, spread, shape, and outliers to judge likelihood? How do they explain the variability?

■ In what circumstances do students add probabilities of simple events? Are they able to identify when events are mutually exclusive (for example, flipping *heads* or *tails*)? When events

are not mutually exclusive (for example, *a one-digit number* and *an odd number*), do they understand why their probabilities cannot be added together to compute the probability that one or the other will occur?

Investigation 2: Fair and Unfair Games

■ How do students interpret the fairness of a game? How do they balance the common sense of the term *fair* with the mathematical sense of fairness? How do they divide their focus between the rules and the results?

■ What approaches do students use to generate a list that includes all the ways an event can occur? How systematic are they? How do they determine that they have generated all the possibilities?

■ How do students apply their knowledge of probability to design a fair game? How do they decide whether or not a game is fair? Do their arguments include mention of rules that give players equal advantage? How do they make sense of uneven results when they play a game they consider to be fair?

■ How do students distinguish between games of chance and games of skill? What common features between games of chance are they able to identify?

■ Do students understand variability in the results of fair games? How do they bring together understandings of the *probability* of a certain set of results, and the effects of chance?

■ How do students go about interpreting and analyzing group data represented on line plots? How do students describe the shape of the data? Do they notice patterns and trends in the data, or do they only look at individual numbers in a data set? Can they judge which data are likely results of a series of probabilistic events?

In the *Investigations* curriculum, mathematical vocabulary is introduced naturally during the activities. We don't ask students to learn definitions of new terms; rather, they come to understand such words as *factor* or *area* or *symmetry* by hearing them used frequently in discussion as they investigate new concepts. This approach is compatible with current theories of second-language acquisition, which emphasize the use of new vocabulary in meaningful contexts while students are actively involved with objects, pictures, and physical movement.

Listed below are some key words used in this unit that will not be new to most English speakers at this age level, but may be unfamiliar to students with limited English proficiency. You will want to spend additional time working on these words with your students who are learning English. If your students are working with a second-language teacher, you might enlist your colleague's aid in familiarizing students with these words, before and during this unit. In the classroom, look for opportunities for students to hear and use these words. Activities you can use to present the words are given in the appendix, Vocabulary Support for Second-Language Learners (p. 74).

certain, always, likely, probable, unlikely, low chance, maybe, impossible, never As students set up a "likelihood line," a continuum to indicate the probability of events happening, they use terms like these to identify how likely or unlikely an occurrence is. These terms are used throughout the unit.

Multicultural Extensions for All Students

Whenever possible, encourage students to share words, objects, customs, or any aspects of daily life from their own cultures and backgrounds that are relevant to the activities in this unit. For example, during the discussion of fair and unfair games in Investigation 2, allow time for students to explain simple games of skill or chance that they play in their families or communities but that may be unfamiliar to others in the class.

Investigations

Finding and Comparing Probabilities

What Happens

Sessions 1 and 2: Creating a Likelihood Line
Students label a class likelihood line with words or phrases ranging from *impossible* to *certain*. Groups brainstorm events that fit each category, trade events with another group, and discuss possible placements along the line. Fractions and decimals are introduced as measures of probability, and students relate these to points on the likelihood line.

Sessions 3 and 4: Using Spinners Students discuss what is meant by the word *probability*. Then pairs spin three spinners 50 times each and plot their results on a common line plot. For each spinner (one-half, one-quarter, and three-quarters green), the students discuss the probability of spinning a green and the number of greens they expect in 50 trials. They find that although few get exactly the expected number in 50 trials, the center of the distribution of the class results is close to the expected number.

Session 5: Testing Guessing Skills Students first discuss homework results and estimate the probability that a tossed bottle cap will land top up. Pairs then test their ability to guess the result of spinning a hidden spinner with four equal sections. The students predict how many correct guesses out of 20 they would expect, assuming average guessing skills, and construct hypothetical line plots of class results based on their predictions. Actual results are also plotted.

Session 6: Guessing Skills Distributions By observing various features of the line plots, students decide which of six hypothetical data sets are real and which are made up. They then judge one more set of results as real or made up; these are revealed to be the results from their own real experiments in the previous session.

Session 7: The Scoring Options Game Student pairs play a spinner game that reviews basic properties of numbers while the players apply what they've learned about probability in a game situation. They may, in the process, learn that selecting the most probable outcome does not guarantee success on a single trial.

Mathematical Emphasis

- Associating the word *probability* with how likely something is to occur
- Associating verbal descriptions with numeric descriptions of probability
- Seeing that repeating a probability experiment several times yields a variety of results
- Using a probability to predict about how often an event will happen in a given number of trials
- Estimating probabilities from results of actual trials
- Predicting and analyzing features of distributions, including center and variability
- Learning to add probabilities of simple events

 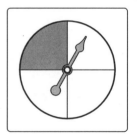

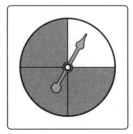

What to Plan Ahead of Time

Materials

- Clear, unmarked spinners: 1 per pair, and 3 demonstration spinners (Sessions 1–5, 7)
- Overhead projector, pens, and transparencies (Session 6; Sessions 1–5 and 7, optional)
- Stick-on notes: 10 per group (Sessions 1–2)
- Large paper (12" by 18"): 1 sheet per group (Sessions 1–2)
- Envelopes: 1 per group (Sessions 1–2)
- Butcher paper or accordion-fold printer paper for making long displays (Sessions 1–5)
- Green markers or crayons (Sessions 3–4)
- Bottle caps: 1 per student, or they supply their own. (Sessions 3–4, homework)

Other Preparation

- Duplicate student sheets and teaching resources (located at the end of this unit) in the following quantities. If you have Student Activity Booklets, copy only the items marked with an asterisk.

For Sessions 1–2

Family letter* (p. 76): 1 per student. Remember to sign it before copying.

Student Sheet 1, The Likelihood Line (p. 77): 1 per student

Student Sheet 2, Creating a Likelihood Line (p. 78): 1 per student (homework)

Student Sheet 3, What Is Probability? (p. 80): 1 per student (homework)

For Sessions 3–4

Spinner Templates (one-half, one-fourth, three-fourths) (p. 88): 1 per pair

Student Sheet 4, Bottle Cap Toss (p. 81): 1 per student (homework)

For Session 5

Guessing Skills Spinner Templates (p. 90): 1 (half-sheet) per pair

For Session 6

Student Sheet 5, Guessing Skills Data for Six Classes (p. 82): 1 per student

For Session 7

Student Sheet 6, Scoring Options Game (p. 83): 1 per pair, and 1 transparency* (optional) of Game A

Student Sheet 7, Scoring Options Challenge (p. 85): as needed

Student Sheet 8, Make Your Own Scoring Options (p. 87): 1 per student (homework)

- If you plan to provide folders in which students will save their work for the entire unit, prepare these for distribution during Session 1.
- Make demonstration spinners from the templates (p. 88), coloring them one-half, one-fourth, and three-fourths green. Have a clear spinner to place over them. (Sessions 1–4)
- Prepare about a 5-foot length of paper for the class likelihood line. (Sessions 1–2)
- Make two blank line plots for display, each about 5 feet long, with a range from 0 to 50, and make another line plot about 2 feet long, with a range from 0 to 20. Use butcher paper, connected sheets of accordion-fold printer paper, or letter-size sheets taped together on the long edges. (Sessions 3–5)

Creating a Likelihood Line

Materials

- Overhead projector and pen (optional)
- Stick-on notes (10 per group)
- Paper, 12 × 18 (1 sheet per group)
- Envelopes (1 per group)
- 5-foot length of paper for likelihood line
- Demonstration spinner, half green
- Student Sheet 1 (1 per student)
- Student Sheet 2 (1 per student, homework)
- Student Sheet 3 (1 per student, homework)
- Family letter (1 per student)

What Happens

Students label a class likelihood line with words or phrases ranging from *impossible* to *certain*. Groups brainstorm events that fit each category, trade events with another group, and discuss possible placements along the line. Fractions and decimals are introduced as measures of probability, and students relate these to points on the likelihood line. Their work focuses on:

- distinguishing events that are certain from those that are not
- learning to associate the word *probability* with how likely something is to occur
- distinguishing among events with different probabilities
- associating verbal descriptions of probability with numeric descriptions
- linking equivalent fractions, decimals, and percents

Setting Up a Likelihood Line

Draw a horizontal line across the board or on an overhead transparency. On the far left, write the word *impossible.*

Today we're going to look at events and discuss how likely or unlikely they are to happen. I've drawn a line that we'll call the likelihood line. At one end, I've written *impossible*. Can you think of any future events that are impossible—events you are sure will never, ever happen?

Take several suggestions and jot them down beneath the word *impossible.* Students may respond by describing a current state of affairs rather than predicting the probability of a future event ("It's impossible that my pen is blue," or "It's impossible that I have a pet cat"). If this happens, make a distinction between what has already happened and what may happen in the future, and explain that, at this point, you are interested in the probability of future events.

What word do you think we should put at the other end of our likelihood line? We need a word that will describe events you are absolutely sure will happen.

Make a list of possibilities, and decide as a class which one to put on the likelihood line. *Certain* is a logical choice, but students may suggest words or phrases that have more meaning for them, such as *definite, gonna happen, 100% sure,* and so on. Throughout this unit, we will use the word *certain* to describe the far right end of the likelihood line. If your students come up with an alternate word or phrase that you would like to use, just substitute that term.

Can you think of any events in the future that are certain—events you're absolutely sure will happen?

Beneath the word *certain,* jot down events the students suggest. Again, emphasize that you are looking for future events. While the statement "It is certain that I am talking" may be true, it does not describe a future event. On the other hand, "It is certain that I will have a birthday next April 24" does describe a future event and therefore meets the criteria.

Over the next couple of weeks, we're going to be studying probability. Learning about probability helps you figure out how likely it is that an event will happen. We'll be particularly interested in studying events that fall somewhere between the points marked *impossible* and *certain,* so we'll need some words to describe the middle ground.

Indicate the approximate midpoint of the likelihood line.

For an event located in the middle here, we would not be surprised if it happened or if it didn't happen. What word should we put here?

Again, students will suggest a variety of words or phrases. As a class, you'll need to pick one that describes a middling probability and add it to the likelihood line. (Throughout this unit, we will use the word *maybe* to describe the midpoint of the likelihood line. Some possible alternatives for *maybe* are *as often as not* and *even chance.*) The class will be catching on by now, so don't spend time attaching events to the midpoint word; students will generate events that match each word or phrase on the likelihood line in the next activity.

Indicate the approximate midpoints between *maybe* and *certain,* and between *impossible* and *maybe.*

Let's add two more words or phrases to the likelihood line. What should we call these points on the line?

Discuss the possibilities. Label the line with words or phrases that your students agree on. These should be similar in meaning to *likely* and *unlikely,* which will be used in this unit. Other possible terms for *likely* are *good chance* and *probable,* and for *unlikely, low chance* and *not often.*

The completed likelihood line should look something like this:

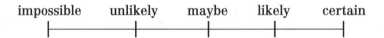

Next, suggest a few ordinary events and ask students to determine where they might go on the line. For example:

> It will snow here on Friday.
>
> The principal will visit our classroom this week.
>
> At least one student in the class will be absent tomorrow.
>
> The sun will come up tomorrow.

Some students may argue that nothing is absolutely certain or impossible. For example, we've had students point out that it's possible the world will blow up today, in which case the sun would *not* come up tomorrow. If students get carried away with these kinds of objections, suggest that some events are close enough to certain or to impossible to justify using those words.

Based on everything we know, it is certain that the sun will come up tomorrow. Although we can't be *absolutely* sure it will happen, the event is much closer to certain than to likely.

Placing Events on the Likelihood Line

With your group, think of two events for each category on the likelihood line. In other words, come up with two events that are impossible, two that are unlikely, and so on. When you finish, you should have ten events.

Later you'll trade events with another group, and they'll have to figure out where your events go on the likelihood line. For that reason, please do *not* include the name of the category in the description of the event, or you'll give away where the event belongs. For example, if you wrote "The sun will definitely come up tomorrow," the word *definitely* gives away that it is a certain event. Instead, write simply "The sun will come up tomorrow."

Each group of three or four students needs at least ten stick-on notes, a piece of 12" × 18" paper for their own likelihood line, and notebook paper for an answer key. With the long paper placed horizontally, students copy along the top the likelihood line the class has developed, leaving plenty of space below for affixing their stick-on notes. Sketch this on the board or show a model so that students are clear on how to proceed.

Write each event on a separate stick-on note and place it on the paper under the likelihood line you have drawn. Make an answer key on a separate piece of paper, and then fold your key so the writing doesn't show.

❖ **Tip for the Linguistically Diverse Classroom** To help with comprehension, all students should include a simple sketch on each stick-on note to illustrate the suggested event.

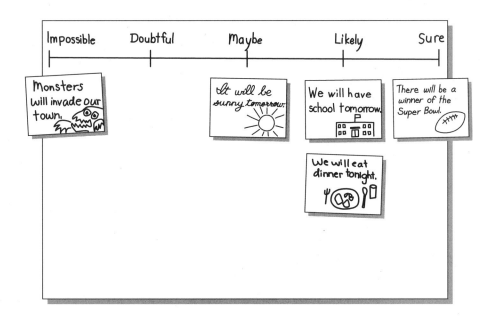

Give each group an envelope. When they have written all their events and made their answer key, groups put their loose stick-on notes and folded keys inside the envelope and write their names on the front. Remind students to mix up their stick-on notes before putting them in the envelope. Groups save their likelihood lines for the next part of the activity.

Trading Events   As the groups finish generating events, they trade envelopes with another group. They then put the new events on their likelihood line in the categories that make sense to them.

When the group is satisfied with the way they have organized the events on the line, they open the answer key and see if their arrangement matches that of the group that brainstormed the events.

If you disagree with another group's placement of an event, write the event and where you think it should go on a piece of paper. We'll discuss different points of view when everyone is finished.

If there is time, stick-on notes can be mixed up again and the envelopes traded between different groups.

Rachel's Group

Answer key
impossible—a male dog will have puppies.
 flowers will talk.
doubtful—a baby will walk at the age of 1 day old.
 the world will blow up tomorrow.
maybe—tomorrow it will rain. we will have a
 fire drill tomorrow.
likely— that we will have music tomorrow.
 we will get chameleons.
100% sure— it will be my birthday in 13 days.
 people will eventually die.

In a class discussion, students ponder the probability of events that have sparked disagreement.

Do you have a different point of view from what was written on an answer key?

Encourage students to explain their reasoning and to address their questions directly to the group they disagree with. Remind them to speak to each other respectfully. It is easier to hear "I disagree with your answer" or "Why did you put it in this category?" than "That's the wrong category!"

During the discussion, you might find it helpful to ask these questions:

If something is unlikely, does that mean it will *never* happen? What do you think when it *does* happen?

If something is likely, does that mean it will *always* happen? What do you think when it *doesn't* happen?

Discussing Different Points of View

Before You Begin   Copy the class likelihood line onto a strip of paper about 5 feet long. Use the same five terms the class proposed in Session 1. Post the line where everyone can see it. If you have space, keep the likelihood line on display for the next several days so you can easily refer to it through the next few sessions.

Call attention to the likelihood line as you begin this activity:

When we first made this likelihood line, we came up with some words to describe different points along it. Sometimes people use numbers instead of words to describe the probability of an event. The number we give to an impossible event is 0. What number do you think is given to a certain event?

Students may have excellent reasons for suggesting a variety of numbers; 100 and 10 are common suggestions. Most often, students have heard probabilities expressed as percents (for example, a 100% chance of rain). Explain that it is also common when speaking of probabilities to use 1 to indicate certainty. In this situation, 1 means the same thing as 100%.

Using Fractions as Measures of Probability

Mathematicians have agreed to assign these particular numbers to the two ends of the likelihood line. They say that *impossible* is a probability of 0, and *certain* is a probability of 1. What number do you think mathematicians give to our word *maybe* on the likelihood line? What about to our word *unlikely?* And our word *likely?*

With guidance from the students, write each of these numbers on the likelihood line, both as fractions and as decimals: 0, ¼ and 0.25, ½ and 0.5, ¾ and 0.75, 1. For more information on how to represent probability, see the two **Teacher Notes,** What's Different About This Unit? (p. 14) and Impossible, Certain, and Everything in Between (p. 15).

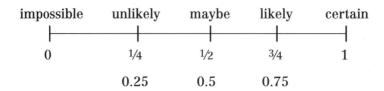

Help students understand that any number along the line can represent a probability.

These are just some of the probabilities we could write on this line. There could be lots of other fractions and decimals on the line between the ones we put up, and I'm sure we could think of lots of other words to go between the words we wrote.

Can anyone tell me a probability somewhere between 0 and ¼? Between ½ and ¾?

When you're thinking about where to put an event on the likelihood line, feel free to use the whole line, not just the five points we labeled.

Now that students have added numerical notation to the likelihood line, some events can be placed more precisely. Begin by asking about an event most students will be able to place:

What number would you use to express the probability of flipping a coin and getting tails? How did you figure this out?

It's important for students to understand that when all the possible results of an event are equally likely (as are heads and tails in coin flipping), the probability of one of those results is expressed this way: the number of ways to achieve that particular result out of the total number of possible results. If students have not had previous experience with this concept, you may need to spend more time on it.

Think about all the possible ways the coin might land. How many ways are there in all? Are both of these equally likely to happen? How many of these are tails? So your chance of landing on tails is one out of two. *[Write the fraction ½ on the board.]* We also call this one-half.

As a class, place these two events on the likelihood line:

What are the chances of rolling a number cube and getting a 1? (1 out of 6)

What are the chances of rolling a number cube and getting either a 1 or a 2? (2 out of 6, or 1 out of 3)

Teacher Checkpoint

Placing Probabilities

Distribute Student Sheet 1, The Likelihood Line. Students label their likelihood lines with the original five categories written on the class line. They write down the word, the fraction, and the decimal for each point.

Each of the events below is preceded by a letter of the alphabet. Ask students to place the letter of each event on their individual likelihood lines at the spot that corresponds to the probability of its happening. Remind students that they can use the entire likelihood line, not just the five points that are labeled.

❖ **Tip for the Linguistically Diverse Classroom** Model each of the following questions as you say them and write them on the board.

What are the chances of

A. flipping a coin and getting heads?
B. rolling a number cube and getting a 6?
C. rolling a number cube once and getting either a 1, 2, or 3?
D. pulling any girl's name out of a container that holds [30] name cards, one for each student in the class?
E. pulling any boy's name out of the same container?
F. pulling *your* name out of the container?
G. spinning this spinner and landing on green? *[Hold up your half-green demonstration spinner.]*

As you say each event, write it on the board. After students have had a minute to place the event on their own likelihood line, call on several students to suggest where to place the event on the class likelihood line and explain their thinking. If there is a disagreement that is not resolved during this discussion, keep all the students' placements on the line: You don't need to decide on one definitive answer. It is more important at this point that students have the chance to explain and revise their reasoning.

After hearing other ideas, allow students to indicate on their own papers that they have changed their minds by placing a letter (for example, a second B) at a new spot and circling it. Students should not erase the original placement of the event. If there is time, students pick one or two events and write about why they placed them where they did.

Collect the students' likelihood lines at the end of class. The lines will offer you a sense of how comfortable your students are using fractions as measures of probability. If your class seems to need more exposure to this idea, begin Session 3 by placing more events on the likelihood line.

❖ **Tip for the Linguistically Diverse Classroom** Again, model each of the questions as you say them and write them on the board.

What are the chances of

H. picking an M out of a box that contains one of each letter of the alphabet?
I.   picking a vowel out of the same box?
J.   picking a consonant out of the same box?

You will need to return the students' likelihood lines in Session 3, as they will continue to add events to them.

Sessions 1 and 2 Follow-Up

Creating a Likelihood Line   Send home the family letter or the *Investigations* at Home booklet after Session 1. Also distribute Student Sheet 2, Creating a Likelihood Line. Explain that for homework students will create a *likelihood line* for where they live. Some examples may be helpful: If it is the middle of winter, it is *likely* that it will rain or snow sometime this week, but it is probably *unlikely* that your street will be renamed this week. Encourage students to generate possibilities with others in the family or in the neighborhood and to come to a common determination of the probability of their occurring.

What Is Probability? After Session 2, distribute Student Sheet 3, What Is Probability? Discuss the assignment with the students, explaining that, after they answer the question, they should have an adult (or perhaps an older sibling) answer it, and then talk together about their responses. Remind students to bring this sheet back to class for use in the next session.

❖ **Tip for the Linguistically Diverse Classroom** Students who are not writing comfortably in English may complete this sheet in their primary language.

Probability and Real-World Risks The probabilities that students encounter in this unit mostly involve events related to spinning spinners and tossing bottle caps—randomizing objects with which they can actually experiment and collect data. Whenever possible, try to extend discussions to introduce some of the real-world events that we often speak of in terms of probability. For example, you might extend these sessions on likelihood this way:

 **Extension**

Suppose I told you that the probability of some event was 1 out of 80. Where would I put this on the likelihood line? Would you think this is a low probability (closer to impossible) or a high probability (closer to certain)?

In the context of other events students have been labeling, they will probably tell you to write this in as a very low probability.

Who can think of an event that can happen—it's not impossible—but that has a very, very low probability?

Students might mention events such as the chance of a tornado hitting their school, or growing up to be 7 feet tall.

Think about this probability: NASA estimates that the probability of a space shuttle flight ending in disaster (as when Challenger exploded after takeoff in 1985) is about 1 in 80. *[Point out where you have written this chance on the class likelihood line.]* **If you were an astronaut on a shuttle flight, would this seem like a low risk to you, or a high risk?**

There is no correct answer here, but the example helps illustrate how relatively small probabilities can still be very important to us. When the event we're talking about is the chance of dying rather than spinning a spinner, a small probability like 1 out of 80 can suddenly seem quite large.

If you have studied probability before, you may be surprised by the focus of this two-week unit.

Probability is often introduced with coins and number cubes, determining how many ways there are for various events to occur. The probability of rolling a 5 with a fair number cube, for example, is ⅙ because it is one of six equally likely numbers you could roll. The probability of rolling an odd number is ³⁄₆ or ½ because, of the six equally likely events, three of them (1, 3, 5) are odd numbers. This way of talking about probability is referred to as *theoretical* probability, because it describes what would happen "in theory" when a number cube is rolled.

However, probability in our lives does not work exactly as it does "in theory." If we actually roll a number cube ten times, we *may* get an odd number exactly half of the time (5 times)—but we may get an odd number only 4 times out of 10 or we may get an odd number 6 times out of 10. This way of talking about probability is referred to as *experimental* probability because it describes what happens when we do an experiment such as rolling a number cube 10 times.

Perhaps the most important concept of this unit is understanding the difference between theoretical and experimental probability. Many of the activities in this unit involve repeating chance events (such as flipping a coin or rolling a number cube) many times. Through these probability experiments, students will be able to see that their results are usually not exactly what they expect according to theoretical probability and that they seldom get identical results when they repeat an experiment.

The experiments students conduct will lead to some questions that get to the heart of the difference between theoretical and experimental probability, e.g., If a coin has a ½ chance of turning up heads on a single flip, why doesn't it turn up heads exactly half of the time? For more help in discussing this distinction with your students, see the **Teacher Note,** Why Doesn't a Half-Green Spinner Spin Green Half the Time? (p. 24).

We all deal with uncertainty in our lives every day, so both you and your students have probably developed everyday intuitions about chance events. Unfortunately, some of the informal, intuitive ideas we form about probability are not in agreement with the mathematics of probability. Be aware of this potential clash—for both you and your students—and realize that it may make learning probability a bit more difficult than other mathematical topics.

You might notice that the unit doesn't include many probabilities of real-world events. This is partly because we want students to discover the meaning of probability through events they can experiment with in the classroom. It's also the case that many of the events important to us have very small probabilities, and developing appropriate intuitions about the meaning of probability with values such as 1 in a million is considerably more difficult than with values such as 1 in 2 or 1 in 4.

Nonetheless, you can link this study of probability to real-world events as suggested in the extension on p. 13. Look for opportunities to introduce a probability associated with a current event that students are aware of, have them locate it on the likelihood line, and discuss what they think the probability value means in that particular situation.

Don't expect your students to understand all the implications of the ideas in this unit. We consider this to be one of several opportunities your students will have to work with probability in their studies of mathematics. The Teacher Notes in the unit highlight the important ideas that you should focus on in your class discussions and in your explorations of probability.

Impossible, Certain, and Everything in Between

The first concept students will meet in this unit is that probability describes different levels of possibility. They discover by considering a variety of future events that some events are impossible, some will definitely occur, and most are somewhere in between. By mathematical convention, we assign 0 as the probability for an event that will never occur and 1 as the probability for an event that will definitely occur. Events in between are given probability values that are fractions between 0 and 1.

For some of the events your students discuss in these beginning sessions, the assigned probability is a matter of opinion until data are collected that allow an estimate. For other events, students can determine the probability theoretically. In both cases, probabilities are expressed as fractions (or decimals).

To understand what these fractions mean, consider the point halfway between 0 and 1. In terms of probability, we label this point ½ or 0.5. We can say, for example, "There is a one-half chance of getting a head when you flip a coin," or "The event has a probability of 0.5." These phrases indicate that heads and tails are equally likely; they have the same probability of occurring.

You can sometimes interpret the fraction ½ as "one out of two," meaning that of the two equally likely ways the coin can land, one of them will result in heads. In the context of probability, reading a fraction in this way is often easier for students to understand than using the term *one-half.* That is, saying "one out of two" helps make the connection between the probability of an outcome and how often it occurs if the event is repeated.

For example, saying that a coin comes up heads one out of two times leads naturally to a prediction that it will come up heads 5 times in 10 flips. However, if someone repeatedly flipped a coin 10 times, there would be many series of 10 throws in which exactly 5 heads did not occur. The relationship between the probability of ½ and what actually happens when a coin is flipped many times is a difficult concept. It is addressed in the **Teacher Note,** Why Doesn't a Half-Green Spinner Spin Green Half the Time? (p. 24).

Although "one out of two" may seem a more natural way for young students to express the probability ½, the phrase can be misleading. It is not always true that an event with a probability of ½ is one of two events, nor that whenever there are two possible events, the probability of each is ½.

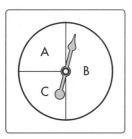 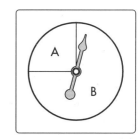

Note that with the left spinner, the probability of B is ½, yet there are three events. With the right spinner, the probability of B is not ½, yet there are two events. The "one out of two" interpretation of a probability of ½ doesn't work when events *are not* equally likely.

Using Spinners

Materials

- Student Sheet 3 homework (for discussion)
- Class likelihood line
- Blank 0-to-50 line plot
- Demonstration spinners, one-half, one-fourth, and three-fourths green
- Clear spinners (1 per pair)
- One-half, one-fourth, and three-fourths spinner templates (1 per pair)
- Green markers or crayons
- Student's completed likelihood lines (on Student Sheet 1)
- Student Sheet 4 (1 per student, homework)
- Bottle caps (1 per student, or they supply their own, homework)
- Overhead projector (optional)

What Happens

Students discuss what is meant by the word *probability*. Then pairs spin three spinners 50 times each and plot their results on a common line plot. For each spinner (one-half, one-quarter, and three-quarters green), the students discuss the probability of spinning a green and the number of greens they expect in 50 trials. They find that although few get exactly the expected number in 50 trials, the center of the distribution of the class results is close to the expected number. Student work focuses on:

- interpreting a probability as a measure or quantity
- seeing that repeating a probability experiment several times yields a variety of results
- using a probability to predict how often an event will happen in a given number of trials
- recording results of probability experiments on line plots
- comparing what is expected with what really happens
- comparing line plots by examining general features

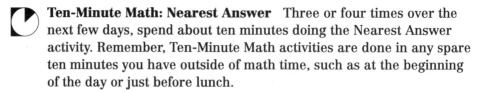 **Ten-Minute Math: Nearest Answer**   Three or four times over the next few days, spend about ten minutes doing the Nearest Answer activity. Remember, Ten-Minute Math activities are done in any spare ten minutes you have outside of math time, such as at the beginning of the day or just before lunch.

Students work mentally, rounding the numbers in computation problems and picking the closest answer from the choices provided. Select two or three Nearest Answer whole number problems (see p. 71) to write on the board or the overhead, or prepare your own problems with four answer choices (one a good estimate, and the others tempting if students do not think carefully).

Show the first problem, keeping the answers covered, for 20 to 30 seconds. Then uncover the answers. Students write down the answer they think is closest. One or two students tell how they rounded the numbers in the problem and chose the nearest answer. Students discuss other ways they did the problem and any disagreements they have.

For complete instructions and variations on this activity, see p. 71.

What We Mean by Probability

Students share the meanings of probability from their Student Sheet 3 homework. You might make two brief lists on the board—one with the students' ideas, and the other with the adults' answers.

Our ideas

- What probably will happen next—

  Probably I'll go to school tomorrow.

Adult ideas

- How likely something is—

  The probability of rain tomorrow is 30%.

Some students may think probability has to do with solving problems (perhaps focusing on the root *prob*), or that it refers only to what is *most likely* to happen. Explain that there are many meanings of the word, but that in this unit, they will be dealing with only one of those meanings.

We will be using the word *probability* as it is used in mathematics. Some of you may not have used it that way before. In mathematics, probability is a measurement or amount. Did any of you or your parents use the word that way? Can you think what probability might be an amount of?

Refer students to the likelihood line and some of the events they placed on it yesterday. Point out to them that the likelihood line looks like a ruler, and that they will be using it to "measure" how often something might happen, or how much belief we have that something is true.

Spinning a One-Half Spinner

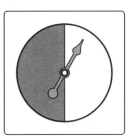

Post the blank 0-to-50 line plot where students can record on it.

In a few minutes, you and a partner will have a chance to spin a spinner like this 50 times. [*Hold up the one-half demonstration spinner.*] You decided earlier that we had a one-half chance of spinning the spinner once and landing on green. What if we spin the spinner 50 times? Do you think the probability of getting green will change? Are the chances still one out of two for each spin?

Discuss this question briefly. Once the class has come to agreement about the probability for a single spin, ask students to predict how many of their 50 spins will land on the green. This time you are looking for an actual number, not a probability.

Students jot down a prediction on a piece of scrap paper and pass it to you. Quickly compile the predictions on the board or overhead. (Don't write students' names next to their predictions, as that could make students less likely to take risks in the future.)

You may hear predictions that are qualified: "It should be 25, but I don't think it usually goes exactly like the chances." Notate such estimates by enclosing the number in parentheses: (25).

Give each pair a one-half spinner template and a clear spinner. They color half the template green (or simply indicate the color by writing out the word). The other half remains blank. Students then place the spinner on top of the template, lining up the outside edges.

Briefly discuss procedures for flicking and reading the spinner. Point out that the spinner is read by looking at where the arrow tip lies. Suggest that students not count a spin unless it goes through several revolutions before it stops, and that they spin on a flat surface, not on their laps.

Spinning 50 Times   In a large class, each pair of students can spin 50 times. With fewer than 30 students, each student should spin 50 times to give the class enough data to analyze. The class as a whole should end up with results from about 800–2000 spins.

Each pair should decide beforehand how they will record their results. Some students keep track by making a mark for each spin and counting as they go along. Others might use tally marks or number a page from 1 to 50. Emphasize to students that their method should allow them to determine when they have completed exactly 50 spins.

Make sure you stop after 50 spins. We want data on just the first 50. If you go over for some reason, you will need to be able to tell which are the extra spins. Decide on a way to record your results that will help you keep track.

When pairs finish spinning, they count how many of their spins landed on the green half of the spinner. They then put an X over that number on the large 0-to-50 line plot. This form of data collection is further discussed in the **Teacher Note**, Line Plot: A Quick Way to Show the Shape of the Data (p. 23).

If some students finish early, consider the extension activity, Collecting Data on Several in a Row (p. 22). Students can continue spinning and keep track of how many times they get two in a row, three in a row, or four in a row of a particular outcome. This can be an ongoing experiment whenever students have extra time following a whole-class activity.

Be sure students save their templates from the one-half spinner for use in Investigation 2.

1 W	26
2 G	27
3 W	28
4 G	29
5 W	30
6 W	31
7 G	32
8 G	33
9 G	34
10 G	35
11 W	36
12 W	37
13 W	38
14 G	39
15	40
16	41
17	42
18	43

One-Fourth and Three-Fourths Spinners

Students now repeat the preceding activity using different spinners. Return their work on Student Sheet 1, The Likelihood Line, and distribute the one-fourth and three-fourths spinner templates for coloring. Pairs should still have their clear spinners.

Hold up the demonstration spinner with one-fourth of the template colored green.

Suppose we use a spinner that looks like this now. If you spin once, what are the chances that you will land on green? (¼) Mark it on your likelihood lines.

Ask a few students to tell where they put the event. Also mark the event on the class likelihood line.

What if you spin this spinner 50 times? How many times do you think you will land on green? Why do you think so?

Again, ask students to jot their predictions on scrap paper. Compile their predictions on the board or overhead. Since ¼ of 50 is 12½, both 12 and 13 are likely predictions, but be prepared for a variety of responses. Keep using the parentheses notation for predictions that reflect what students think "should" happen, but not necessarily what they believe will actually occur during a trial of 50 spins.

Before the students spin the one-fourth spinner, repeat the prediction procedure for the three-fourths spinner. (Making both predictions before spinning lets students work uninterrupted for a longer period of time.) Ask students to predict both the probability of landing on green in one spin and the number of times the spinner will land on green in 50 spins.

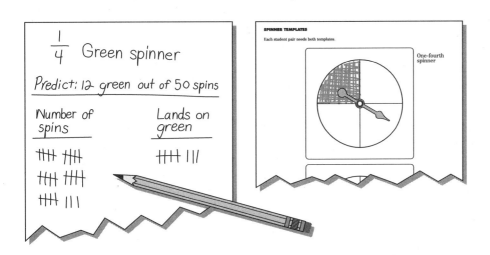

Students now work with the new spinner templates, spinning each one 50 times in turn. Some students may suggest that data for the three-fourths spinner could be obtained by subtracting the data for the one-fourth spinner from 50. This is an important insight to discuss with the class. However, tell those students you would still like them to use the three-fourths spinner to generate another set of data so they will experience different ways the data might fall.

As they finish, students again use the class line plot at the front of the room to record the number of times out of 50 the spinners landed on the green section. Use the same line plot to record the results of all three spinners. To eliminate confusion, use different symbols or different-colored markers to record the results from the three spinners.

Students who finish early can continue spinning to look for the frequency of two-, three-, or four-in-a-row outcomes.

Note: Be sure students keep their individual likelihood lines for further use in Session 5.

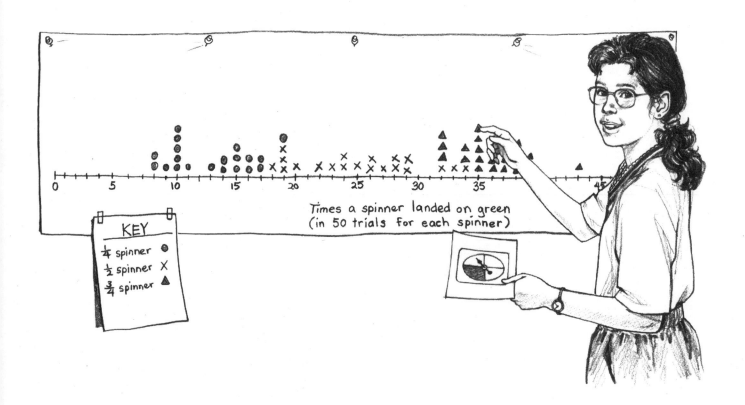

Times a spinner landed on green
(in 50 trials for each spinner)

KEY

$\frac{1}{4}$ spinner ●
$\frac{1}{2}$ spinner ✕
$\frac{3}{4}$ spinner ▲

How would you describe the shape of the data for the spinner that was half green?

Discussing the Spinner Results

See the **Teacher Note,** Interpreting Line-Plot Distributions (p. 36), for information about how to help students get information from line plots. Students are likely to refer at first to specific scores rather than general features. If so, ask some questions that help focus attention on more general aspects of the data:

What's in the middle of the line plot? If you could draw a straight vertical line that divides the data about in half, where would it be?

Many of you predicted that if you spun the one-half spinner 50 times, you'd get green 25 times. Why does our line plot look the way it does? Does it surprise you that everybody didn't land on green 25 times?

The **Dialogue Box,** Discussing Spinner Results (p. 26), demonstrates one teacher's handling of this class discussion. Most students will probably understand that while 25 is the most reasonable prediction, it doesn't always work out that exactly 25 out of 50 spins land on green. The question is why we predict 25, and what this has to do with the probability $\frac{1}{2}$.

Can someone summarize what this line plot tells us?

The two most important features are the fact that the data are not all located on the expected number, 25, and that the center (median) of the data is very close to this value, which we expect based on the probability of $\frac{1}{2}$. For more information on the relationship between probability and what actually happens, see the **Teacher Note,** Why Doesn't a Half-Green Spinner Spin Green Half the Time? (p. 24).

What about the one-fourth spinner and the three-fourths spinner results? Were these what you expected?

What's about in the middle of the results for the one-fourth spinner? for the three-fourths spinner? If you could draw a straight vertical line that divides the data about in half for each set of results, where would it be? (The center of the class data for the one-fourth spinner should be close to 12$\frac{1}{2}$, or $\frac{1}{4}$ of 50; for the three-fourths spinner, close to 37$\frac{1}{2}$, or $\frac{3}{4}$ of 50.)

Keep the line plot posted throughout the unit so students will have examples of data distributions handy. However, be careful not to conclude too much from the three sets of data you obtained. If you repeated these spinner activities, the new plot could look quite different from your original results.

Sessions 3 and 4 Follow-Up

Homework

Bottle Cap Toss   After Session 4, distribute Student Sheet 4, Bottle Cap Toss. You might also distribute bottle caps so each student will use the same kind of cap, but this is not necessary. Flat metal caps, like those on juice bottles, work well. Plastic caps with straight sides are not recommended as they can land on their sides as well as top up or top down; if students use one of these, they may simply ignore the trials when the cap lands on its side.

❖ **Tip for the Linguistically Diverse Classroom**   Model the instructions as you read aloud Student Sheet 4.

At home, students are to toss their bottle cap into the air and let it land on the floor 50 times. As they toss, they record how many times the cap lands with the top up and how many times it lands with the top down. They then repeat the activity, tossing the bottle cap another 50 times. They bring to class two separate sets of data, one for each series of 50 tosses. If time allows, ask students to predict the results before they go home.

Extension

Collecting Data on Several in a Row   As students spin a one-half spinner 50 times, they keep track of how many times they get two in a row, three in a row, four in a row, or five in a row of a particular outcome. If students keep track horizontally on a single strip of paper, such as adding machine tape, they might spot patterns more easily. Students can circle the runs—occurrences of several in a row—using different colors for runs of different lengths, and then hang their strips around the room. As always, the more data the class collects, the better. After the data have been collected, ask your students how common or uncommon it is to encounter runs of two in a row, three in a row, and so on. Most people are quite surprised by how common it is to get fairly long runs in random data.

Line Plot: A Quick Way to Show the Shape of the Data

A line plot is a quick way to organize numerical data. It clearly shows the range of the data and how the data are distributed over that range. Line plots work especially well for numerical data with a small range.

When a line plot is made informally for your own use (rather than for use in a presentation), it does not need a title, labels, or a vertical axis. A line plot is simply a sketch showing the values of the data along a horizontal axis with X's or some other symbol marking the occurrence of those values in the data set.

For example, suppose 15 students have just collected data on the number of times out of 50 spins that a one-fourth spinner lands on green. A line plot of their data might look like this:

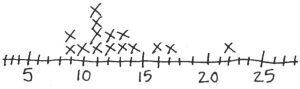

Although the range is from 9 to 22, most of the data fall between 9 and 14. The outlier, at 22, appears to be an unusual value, separated by a considerable gap from the rest of the data. The median is 12 (half of the values are 12 or less, and half are 12 or more).

One advantage of a line plot is that you can record each piece of data as you collect it. If you use line plots in this way, you will need to start with an initial guess from students about what the range of the data is likely to be.

What do you think the lowest number should be? How high should we go?

Leave some room on each end of the line plot so that you can lengthen the line if the range includes lower or higher values than you expected.

By sketching data in line plots on the chalkboard, you show students how such plots can quickly provide a clear picture of the shape of the data.

Why Doesn't a Half-Green Spinner Spin Green Half the Time?

What does it mean to have a 1 out of 2, or 50 percent, chance? Does it mean that a coin comes up heads exactly 50 percent of the time? If you toss a coin 10 times, do you think you will always get 5 heads? If you got heads 6 times out of 10 on one set of flips, would you question the fairness of that coin?

Your intuition about these questions probably tells you that a 1 out of 2 chance does not mean the outcome will be exactly 50 percent. Most of us feel comfortable if a fair coin actually turns up 6 or even 7 heads on 10 flips. But 10 heads out of 10 makes us suspicious. We don't demand that a coin always turn up exactly 5 out of 10 heads to call it fair—but if it repeatedly lands more often on heads or tails, we begin to suspect that the coin is not fair.

Here's how these intuitions fit into the mathematical concept of probability. The theoretical probability of landing heads on one flip of a fair coin is 0.5, or 50 percent, or 1 out of 2. If we flip the coin 10 times, we have an expectation that 1 out of 2 flips will be heads, so that we expect to get 5 heads out of 10. We call 5 heads in this case the *expected number*.

When we actually flip the coin 10 times, however, we may well get some other result—4 heads, 6 heads, even occasionally 8 heads out of 10. If we repeated a series of 10 flips 100 times, we could keep track of how many times we got each possible result. We are likely (but not guaranteed) to get 5 heads out of 10 more frequently than any other result—with 4 or 6 heads next most likely, 3 or 7 next most likely, and so on. We could then make a plot of how often we got each number of heads. The graph at right shows the results we got when we repeated a series of 10 flips of a coin 100 times.

The most important things to notice about this graph are as follows:

- Five heads is one of the most frequent results (24 of the 100 trials resulted in 5 heads).

- The distribution is centered around 5 (the median is exactly 5, and the mean is 4.98).

- The distribution is roughly symmetrical around the center value of 5.

- The distribution is generally mound-shaped. The farther it gets from 5 out of 10, the fewer occurrences there are. Beyond a certain point, there are very few occurrences. We got 1 head once, 9 heads twice, and never 0 or 10 heads. These extreme results are very unlikely and thus surprise us when they happen.

To return to the question we raised in the beginning: If a probability doesn't tell us precisely what will happen, what does it tell us? While we can't predict for a given set of 10 flips exactly what we'll get, we do know something about a large collection of sets of 10 flips. We know, for example, that the results for the collection will be centered around 5 out of 10, so 5 is our best guess about what will occur in any single set of 10 flips.

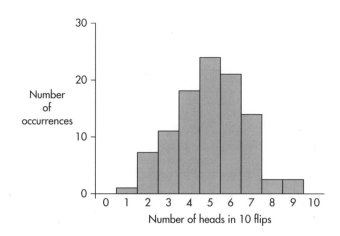

Continued on next page

We can think of the meaning of a probability of ½ in several different ways. Here are three of them:

■ Sometimes we can figure out a probability theoretically. In this case, to say that the probability of heads is ½ means simply that there are two sides of the coin, and each one is equally likely to occur (assuming the coin is fair).

■ The probability allows us to compute the expected number of occurrences of heads if we flip the coin a certain number of times. And if we actually conduct trials, we expect that the distribution of results will be centered around the expected number.

In our coin example above, the expected number is 5 heads, and our distribution of 100 series of 10 flips is indeed centered around 5. If we repeated the 10 flips 1000 times, we would be even more likely to get a distribution of results centered around 5.

■ If we were to repeatedly flip a fair coin a large number of times, the occurrence of heads would get closer and closer to ½ or 50 percent. This is one way that formal probability theory connects a theoretical probability of ½ with what actually happens when a coin is tossed. If we continue flipping indefinitely, we get closer and closer to ½.

Note that this does *not* mean, as many people think, that the actual numbers of heads and tails get closer as we toss more. The actual numbers, in fact, tend to get further apart. How can this be, if the percentage of heads and tails gets closer?

The table below shows actual results of flipping a coin. We recorded the number of heads, the difference between the number of heads and tails, and the percentage of heads after 10, 100, and 1000 flips. As the sample size gets larger, the percentage of heads gets closer to 50 percent, while the actual numbers of heads and tails grow further apart.

Number of flips	Number of heads	Number of heads minus number of tails	Percent of heads
10	6	2	60%
100	56	12	56%
1000	513	26	51%

In the activities in this unit, students encounter two basic ideas. The first is that there are many times when you do *not* get the expected number of outcomes. We will refer to this concept as "spread." The second is that although you can't predict exactly what will happen on a single trial or even a series of trials, you can be fairly certain that if you do many series of trials, the distribution of results will have a center (median and mean) that is quite close to the expected number—the number we compute using the probability. So, for example, in many series of 10 flips of a coin, the distribution of results will have a center quite close to ½.

□D□I□A□L□O□G□U□E□ □B□O□X□

Discussing Spinner Results

This class is discussing the results pairs got from spinning the half-green spinner 50 times (p. 17).

```
              X
          X  X X
          X  X X
          X  X X X  X X
 X        X X X X  X X                              X
 ──────────────────────────────────────────────────────────
 19 20 21 22 23 24 25 26  27 28  29  30 31  32 33 34 35
```

How do our results compare to what we expected?

Noah: Most of us got 23, 25, or 26. And that's about what we predicted.

Cara: Except for the 35.

Noah: No, but remember, we said that it wouldn't work out exactly 25 for everyone, and it didn't. So, we did get what we expected.

Cara, are you saying that the 35 surprised you? And how about the 19?

Cara: The 19 seems like it wouldn't be that hard to get, but the 35 is way, way out there—really far from the rest of the scores, from the 25.

Mei-Ling: When we got it, we thought something was wrong with our spinner, but we did it again and got 23 the second time.

Are there any other ways to explain the 35?

Leon: Maybe whoever was spinning, they weren't spinning hard enough.

Natalie: Or maybe they counted wrong.

Tai: I was keeping track, and I know it was 35.

Any other possible ways to explain the 35? [long pause] What do you think the probability is of getting a 35 if the spinner and everything else is working as it should? That is, what's the probability of it just happening because of chance?

Natalie: Pretty low.

Manuel: Yeah, but it could happen. And maybe this was one of those times.

Did anything else surprise you?

Matt: Yeah. I didn't think anyone would spin exactly one-half. When Katrina got exactly 25, I was really surprised.

Why?

Matt: 'Cause I thought there was very little chance of getting exactly what you expect. Things hardly ever work out perfectly.

Trevor: Well, but it's not like the spinner is thinking, "Don't come out exactly even," so 25 should be as likely as any other result.

Do you think, Trevor, that 25 is *more* likely than other results?

Trevor: Well, more likely than say 30, or 20, but maybe not much different than other scores right around 25.

Can someone summarize what we found, referring to our line plot?

Jasmine: You don't always get the same thing.

Can you say that and refer to our results?

Jasmine: We got results all the way from 19 to 35, but most of them were pretty close to 25.

Zach: The results are spread out, but most are in the middle.

Shakita: Most of the scores are close to 25, and that's one-half. That's what we predicted.

The teacher picked up on Cara's mention of the outlier 35 to help students see that they need not account for such scores by questioning the fairness of the spinner. It is fairly typical to get a few scores out at the extremes when we conduct a chance experiment many times.

The teacher then helped the students attend to more general features of the results. This is important, because many students will focus on a single feature of the data, such as one score that seems especially far out, or the clump in the center. When students are encouraged to share what they see, they can begin to develop their ability to see multiple features.

Testing Guessing Skills

What Happens

Students first discuss homework results and estimate the probability that a tossed bottle cap will land top up. Pairs then test their ability to guess the result of spinning a hidden spinner with four equal sections. The students predict how many correct guesses out of 20 they would expect, assuming average guessing skills, and construct hypothetical line plots of class results based on their predictions. Actual results are also plotted. Student work focuses on:

- estimating probabilities from results of actual trials
- inferring a theoretical probability from looking at a spinner divided into sectors
- computing an expected number from a probability
- predicting and analyzing features of distributions, including center and variability

Materials

- Class likelihood line
- Students' likelihood lines (on Student Sheet 1)
- Blank 0-to-50 line plot
- Blank 0-to-20 line plot
- Guessing skills spinner template (1 per pair)
- Clear spinners (1 per pair)
- Overhead projector (optional)

Activity

Organizing the Bottle Cap Data

Tape up a blank line plot with a range from 0 to 50. Each student marks an X on the line plot to show how many times out of 50 his or her bottle cap landed with the top up. Once all the data have been represented, students use the results to try to estimate the probability of the bottle cap landing top up.

Did any of you change your minds about the probability as a result of actually tossing the bottle cap?

Some students will have predicted that the probabilities of the two possible positions are equal, so that each is ½. This is a reasonable starting point. In actually doing the activity, students will see, as they did with the ¼ and ¾ spinners, that when an event has two possible outcomes, the outcomes are not necessarily equally likely. With the spinners, we can compare the areas of the two events to figure out logically what the probabilities are. With the bottle caps, about all we can do is collect data and base our estimates of probability on them.

Let's add bottle cap tossing to the class likelihood line, based on the results you got as a class. What do you think the chances are of the cap landing with the top up when you toss it and let it land on the floor?

If students have difficulty finding the approximate fraction from the data they collected, help them with questions such as the following:

Do you think the probability of the cap landing top up is about ½? Is it lower or higher than ½? Is it between 0 and ¼, or between ¼ and ½?

Students also add this event to their individual likelihood lines.

Note: From our experience, bottle caps of various types are about twice as likely to land with the top down as with the top up. Differences in the shape and material of the cap, however, appear to affect the probability. If you have time, students could investigate whether there are apparent differences in the results based on the type of bottle cap used.

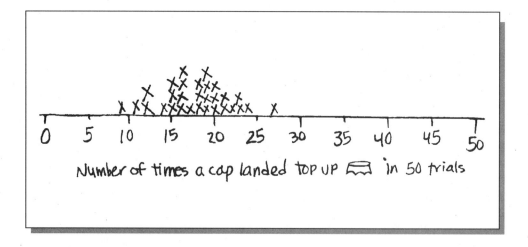

Activity

Testing for Special Guessing Skills

Lots of the games we play are guessing games, like Twenty Questions or Hangman [use the names of guessing games familiar to your students]. Usually, we are not doing pure guessing; there are some clues to help us make "smart" guesses. But suppose there were no clues at all—then how good at guessing do you think you would be?

Today we are going to do an experiment, using spinners, to find out how good you are as pure guessers. We will also learn something about how we can use probability to investigate such a question.

Show the guessing skills template, which is divided into four equal sections. Each section contains a different symbol: a star, a circle, a square, and a triangle.

Demonstrating the Activity Choose two volunteers to demonstrate the activity in front of the class as you explain it. Students work in pairs, sitting back to back. The student with the spinner should have a flat surface to work on.

■ Before beginning, each student numbers a piece of paper from 1 to 20. Students will use this sheet to record the results of their own guessing.

■ Student 1 spins the spinner and, when it stops, says, "Ready for a guess."

■ Student 2 guesses which of the four symbols the spinner landed on and records the guess on the numbered sheet.

■ Student 1 announces whether the guess is right or wrong, but if the guess is wrong, does *not* reveal the correct symbol.

■ Student 2 records whether his or her response was right or wrong (you might establish a shorthand system, such as a check mark for right and an X for wrong). This continues for 20 trials, at which point the two students switch roles. (For the demonstration, they do only about 6 trials.)

Possible Variation Some teachers have done this activity as it is written, as a test of guessing skills. Others have introduced it by asking students whether they think some people have the ability to "read minds." They then conducted the activity as a test of students' "mind-reading skills," in which the student who has the spinner tries to mentally "send" to his or her partner the shape that the spinner has landed on. Either of these scenarios will work for the activity, and the data you could expect students to collect under either condition will be the same.

Predicting Results   After the demonstration, but before students begin the activity, ask them to predict how good they will be at guessing. That is, what is the probability of getting a right answer, even if they are not especially good guessers? It is important not to skip this step; students should expect that even the worst guessers will get a certain number of right answers just by chance.

Suppose you have no special guessing skills. Could you be right about the spinner just by chance? If you have no special guessing skills, what is the probability of a guess being correct on one trial? (1/4) Add this event to your likelihood line.

As students put this event on their own likelihood line, add it to the class likelihood line.

In 20 trials, how many times do you think you'd guess right just by chance?

Since the probability of correctly guessing a spin is 1/4, the expected number of correct guesses in 20 spins is 1/4 of 20, or 5. See the **Dialogue Box,** What to Expect from the Guessing Skills Experiment (p. 32), for some ideas about this discussion.

Ask the students to imagine what results for the entire class might look like.

Let's suppose no one in the class has special guessing skills—that is, whenever we happen to be right about the spinner on a particular trial, it is the result of pure chance and not any special skills. Draw a line plot showing what the results for the whole class might look like in this case. We'll call this a "hypothetical" line plot. Be sure to include an X for every person in the class.

Students plot the results they would expect from a class with no special guessing skills, marking an X for each expected score (number of correct

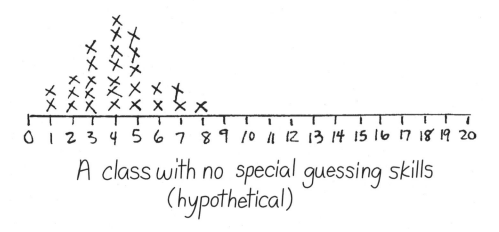

A class with no special guessing skills
(hypothetical)

guesses in 20 trials). Ask three or four volunteers to copy their hypothetical line plots on the board or overhead for the class to see.

Briefly discuss the differences in the distributions students have drawn. Ask questions about the center, the range, and the shape of the data. For information about some of the important features to discuss, see the **Teacher Note**, Interpreting Line-Plot Distributions (p. 36).

Where is the center of your hypothetical line plot? Does the data pile up in the middle or spread itself out? What is the range?

Explore with your students what scores would suggest that someone had special guessing skills.

What score would indicate to you that someone might have special guessing skills? Do you think someone could get 6 right just by chance? What about 8? 12? 15? What number of correct answers would make you think someone had special guessing skills?

Conducting the Experiment   Student pairs test each other's guessing skills, following the demonstrated procedure. Post the 0-to-20 blank line plot. As students finish, they put an X on this line plot to indicate their score (the number of times they guessed correctly). Save the completed line plot for discussion during the next session.

As pairs complete the task, ask them to compare their results to their predictions.

Is your score in the range you predicted for someone without special guessing skills?

Note: After class, create a transparency that shows this same class data on an unlabeled line plot like those on Student Sheet 5. Title it "Line Plot for Class G." You will be presenting this along with the hypothetical data from six other classes, and you will not tell students that this one is theirs.

Session 5 Follow-Up

Matching Spinners   To help students understand what results they might expect to get by chance, have them spin two spinners to see how often one spinner will "predict" the results of the other spinner. Students could work in groups of four, with two students spinning, one student checking for matches, and one recording the results. If students do 20 trials, they could compare the results with those they obtained in the guessing skills experiment.

 **Extension**

What to Expect from the Guessing Skills Experiment

This class is discussing what types of scores they might expect to see in the guessing skills experiment they are about to do.

What if you had no special guessing skills— how do you think you'd do on the 20 trials?

Katrina: You wouldn't get any right.

Maricel: I think you could get some right, because sometimes you'll just happen to get it right, like when you guess which way a coin lands.

Matt: Yeah, but this isn't a coin. This has four sides, so it's going to be much harder to get it right.

What is the probability of guessing correctly on one spin?

Matt: Well, the spinner has four … it's 1 of 4, I guess.

Danny: Maybe less though, because you're going to be guessing a different one each time, and the spinner will be landing different each time, so…

Rachel: But that still works out to 1 out of 4. I mean, there are only four different shapes it can be, and when I guess one of them, it has a probability of one-fourth of being the right one.

Based on Rachel's analysis, the class determines that out of 20 trials, they would expect about a fourth of the trials, or 5, to be correct—even without especially good guessing skills. The teacher continues:

Suppose we gave an award to people who are super guessers. What score would we say makes you a super guesser? *[pause]* **We said that we wouldn't be surprised at all for someone to get 5 right. They could do that just by chance. Could they get 6 by chance?**

Marcus: Well, sure. That's so close to 5.

Heather: I would say about 7 and higher makes you a super guesser. If you have more than 5, that's more than you're supposed to get. Maybe 8 … or 10 and higher.

Antonio: Anywhere from 17 to 20.

Becky: Well, even someone who was a super guesser probably won't get them all correct, so maybe down to 15 would be a good cutoff score.

Could someone get 15 out of 20 just by chance?

Becky: Well, there's some probability of that happening, but still I'd start thinking, "Hey, this guy's awfully good."

The teacher doesn't push the students to decide on the exact score at which they would deem someone a "super guesser." The important point is that some people will get relatively high scores purely by chance. To see this, students must first determine the *expected* number of correct responses, assuming a probability of 1/4 of guessing correctly. This expected number of 5 out of 20 becomes a reference point for the discussion of guessing skills data from several different classes in Session 6.

Guessing Skills Distributions

What Happens

By observing various features of the line plots, students decide which of six hypothetical data sets are real and which are made up. They then judge one more set of results as real or made up; these are revealed to be the results from their own real experiments in the previous session. Student work focuses on:

■ judging likelihood of data based on characteristic features, such as center, spread, shape, outliers

■ comparing predicted to actual results

Materials

■ Student Sheet 5 (1 per student)

■ Transparency with un-labeled line plot of the class guessing skills results from Session 5

■ Overhead projector

Refer to the posted 0-to-20 line plot of the class guessing skills data from Session 5.

Let's look more closely at your scores in the guessing skills experiment, and see how you rate as a class of guessers. What do you notice about this line plot? What's the range? Where's the center? Is it near where you thought the center might be?

Even though students may have agreed beforehand that it is likely for several people to get scores above the expected value by chance, it will be tempting to be really impressed by the guessing skills of the highest scorers. It is not unusual for a class to get a few scores of 9 or 10. Remind students of the discussion in the previous session, when they talked about what score might qualify someone as having special guessing skills.

If a student had especially good guessing skills, we would expect him or her to do consistently better than chance. If students are eager to retest the high scorers to see if they can consistently make better-than-average guesses, wait until after the next activity to do so.

Looking at the Guessing Skills Results

Judging Results: Likely or Unlikely?

Distribute Student Sheet 5, Guessing Skills Data for Six Classes.

Some of the line plots on this page show data from real classrooms. Just like you, the students in those classes did 20 trials of the guessing skills experiment, trying to guess what symbol came up on the hidden spinner. Each X stands for one student, and it shows the student's score—how many times the student guessed the right symbol.

However, some of the line plots on this sheet are made up—they do *not* represent real data. In fact, they were specifically set up to show *unlikely* results. With your group, look at each line plot and decide: Is this one real or made up?

In groups of four, students discuss and decide whether or not the data seem believable—is each set of results likely or unlikely to occur? Students base their decisions on the data they collected for their own guessing skills experiment and on their own expectations of how the data should be distributed. Remind the class to pay attention to the shape of the line plot as well as to the values of the X's. On the student sheet, next to each plot, the students write whether it seems likely or unlikely and note their reasons for that decision.

When groups have finished, discuss their conclusions as a class. The **Teacher Note,** Interpreting Line-Plot Distributions (p. 36), describes the key features of each line plot and gives information about why it is more or less likely. It is important for everyone to recognize that each of these line plots is indeed *possible,* but some are much more likely than others. Thus, avoid asking, "Could these results really happen?" because in fact they *could.* Use wording like this instead: "Are these results *likely* to happen?" or "Would you be suspicious of these results?"

Since students have had limited experience with line plots in this unit, they might conclude that a particular plot is not likely because it doesn't closely match what they have seen. Students may think that the range should be the same as in their class, or argue that because *they* got three 7's and there are no 7's in these data, the data must be made up. Students might also be misled by the presence of relatively few X's on the expected value. Help these students focus on important aspects of the line plots, but point them out without offering any conclusions. For example:

Where is the center in this line plot? Is this likely or unlikely? What do you think about the shape of the line plot?

The **Dialogue Box,** Which Data Are Made Up? (p. 39), shows how one teacher carefully redirected student attention.

Although the **Teacher Note** (p. 36) reveals which of the six line plots are real and which are made up, be cautious about sharing this information, especially when students are wrong. The goal is to get students to notice patterns and revise their theories over time as they continue to work with data and probability. You can encourage this kind of thinking by starting a list of questions or hypotheses at the front of the room, drawing from what the students observe. For example:

I think it is unlikely to have a gap in the data.

Real data would never include a 0 or 1.

You can return to this list repeatedly throughout the unit as students adjust their ideas.

Once students have decided about the six plots, show your transparency of your class's guessing skills data from the previous session.

I have one more line plot to show you. Do you think this one is real or made up?

After hearing several points of view, inform students that this line plot shows their class's data. (If you still have the large class line plot posted, students can confirm that they are the same.) Looking again at the distribution of their own real data may cause some students to rethink what types of line plots are possible or likely.

Session 6 Follow-Up

Extension

Retesting High Scorers Ask students to look again at the class line plot to find the highest scores.

Do any of these scores seem too good to be true? Is there anyone you would like to retest?

Ask these students if they would mind being retested. You can either retest the high scorers in front of the class or have them repeat the experiment more privately at some other time, depending on the schedule and the students' preferences. Alternatively, you could test the entire class over again, and compare the two sets of results for each student.

It is likely that students who scored high the first time will not do so well on retesting, and students who had low scores the first time will tend to do better in the second testing. This is a statistical principle called "regression to the mean." However, a person's score will sometimes remain quite high or low a second time, by chance.

The primary purpose of focusing on line-plot distributions is to encourage students to attend to general features of data, including the *center, shape, range, outliers,* and *gaps,* and to use these features in arguing whether the data seem likely to be based on real occurrences. You might need to help some students formulate their reasons in terms of the features described below.

Range   The range of the data is the interval from the lowest score to the highest score in the data set. For example, the range in plot A is from 2 to 9.

Shape   We can think of shape as what we would get if we drew a smooth line over the top of the data. For example, the shape of the data in plot A suggests a mound, with most of the data piled up over the middle values, and smaller amounts of the data spread out over values on either side. In plot D, the data are spread rather evenly over the whole range, nearly forming a rectangle. In plot B, the data are shaped like a ramp, slanting down from the lower to the higher values. In plot C, the data are in a spike, with very little spread.

Gap   A gap is a visible "hole" in the data—a value or a range of values where there are no scores. Plots B and F both have a gap at the value 8. Some students believe that gaps don't occur in real data, but real plot E—with a gap at 10—shows that they do.

Outlier   An outlier is a score that is either considerably higher or considerably lower than the other scores. There is no one definition of how far away from the rest of the data a score must be to be considered an outlier. In this exercise, it should be left up to the students to decide. In line plot B, the score of 9 might be considered an outlier. Outliers are often of particular interest. Sometimes they occur because of errors in recording. Other times, they are not errors but unusual cases that deserve special consideration.

Center   There are a number of different ways to describe the center of the data. Some students might focus only on the value that has the most X's, or the *mode.* Many will focus on the midpoint of the range, and therefore see the center of plot B as 4 or 5 because those values are midway between the lowest and highest values, 1 and 9. The mode and the midpoint of the range are not particularly powerful descriptors of the center. The midpoint of the range ignores all the data except the two extremes. Similarly, the mode is determined only by the data at one point of the distribution.

The best measure of center for students working in this unit is the *median.* The median is the value that divides the data into upper and lower halves. If we wanted to determine the median precisely, we would order the data from smallest to largest and find the value of the middle piece of data. Students have learned in previous units to determine the median exactly using this technique.

At this point, students should develop a more advanced skill: estimating the median using a visual sense of where the data are centered. We can do this by thinking about where we would draw a line vertically through a line plot so that roughly equal numbers of X's are on each side of the line, as shown below.

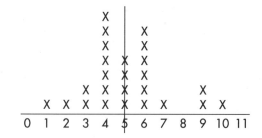

In plot F, for example, we would like students to notice, without necessarily counting up scores, that the median is about 3, lower than the expected number, 5.

Continued on next page

Description of Distributions on Student Sheet 5 Following are the characteristics you want to help students notice in the plots on Student Sheet 5.

Plots A, E: These are actual data. Notice that actual scores from this experiment range over several values, do have gaps (plot E), and that the value we expect to occur, 5, does not always occur most frequently (plot E). However, the center and shape are what we expect.

Plot B: Although the range is roughly what we expect, the shape is not. The data are bunched up on the lower end of the plot rather than in the center. As a result, the median of the data is lower than we expect—around 2 or 3 rather than 5.

Plot C: The data are centered around 5, but they are more bunched up in the middle and have a smaller range than we expect.

Plot D: Even though the range and center of these data appear reasonable, the shape is not what we would expect. The scores are not bunched up in the middle, but rather are spread more evenly over the range.

Plot F: The shape of this plot is reasonable, but the median of the data is lower than we would expect.

This discussion works better if you do not tell the students beforehand which plots were made up and which were not. You can reveal this if you wish after students have made their arguments.

Line plot A

```
                    X
                    X
                    X  X
                 X  X  X
                 X  X  X
              X  X  X  X        X
              X  X  X  X  X  X  X
  0  1  2  3  4  5  6  7  8  9 10 11
```

Line plot B

```
  X
  X
  X  X
  X  X  X  X
  X  X  X
  X  X  X        X
  X  X  X  X  X  X        X
  0  1  2  3  4  5  6  7  8  9 10 11
```

Line plot C

```
              X
              X
              X  X
           X  X  X
           X  X  X
           X  X  X
           X  X  X
           X  X  X
           X  X  X
           X  X  X
  0  1  2  3  4  5  6  7  8  9 10 11
```

Line plot D

```
           X              X
           X     X  X  X  X  X
        X  X  X  X  X  X  X  X
        X  X  X  X  X  X  X  X  X
  0  1  2  3  4  5  6  7  8  9 10 11
```

Line plot E

```
              X
           X  X
           X  X
        X  X  X
        X  X  X     X
     X  X  X  X  X  X     X
  0  1  2  3  4  5  6  7  8  9 10 11
```

Line plot F

```
           X
           X
        X  X  X
     X  X  X  X
     X  X  X  X  X
  X  X  X  X  X  X     X
  0  1  2  3  4  5  6  7  8  9 10 11
```

Continued on next page

More Real Data   To give you a better idea of what you might expect to observe in your classroom, we have included below six more "real" distributions. These were obtained not from classrooms but from a computer's prediction of what symbols were spun. All else remains the same: Each X represents a student who tried on 20 occasions to guess which of four symbols had been spun. Each line plot represents a class of 25 students. Since the computer has a ¼ chance of being correct, we expect the median of the distribution of results to be near 5 (¼ of 20).

You might expect to see any of these distributions in your own class data. Notice that most of the distributions are mound shaped, although plot 1 is quite different from what we would expect to get. In these plots, 5 is not always the mode. Even when distributions look odd, however, the median will still tend to be 5 (it is in every one of these distributions).

Also, it is not that unusual in a class of 25 to have at least one student who gets 10 or more correct. This happened in 3 of our 6 computer-modeled classrooms. If your class has more than 25 students, you're even more likely to get at least one student guessing correctly 10 or more times. We can compute that the probability of getting 13 or more correct is quite low, however—roughly 1 in 6000. As low as this probability is, it tells us that for every 6000 students who do this experiment, we expect one student to get at least 13 correct just by chance.

Line plot 1

```
              X  X     X
              X  X     X
              X  X     X
              X  X     X
           X  X  X     X        X
           X  X  X  X  X  X  X  X
  ─────────────────────────────────────
   0  1  2  3  4  5  6  7  8  9 10 11
```

Line plot 2

```
                    X
                    X
                 X  X
                 X  X
                 X  X
                 X  X  X     X
           X  X  X  X  X  X  X
           X  X  X  X  X  X  X
  ─────────────────────────────────────
   0  1  2  3  4  5  6  7  8  9 10 11
```

Line plot 3

```
              X
              X     X
              X     X
              X  X  X
              X  X  X
           X  X  X  X        X
     X  X  X  X  X  X  X     X  X
  ─────────────────────────────────────
   0  1  2  3  4  5  6  7  8  9 10 11
```

Line plot 4

```
              X
              X  X
              X  X
           X  X  X  X
           X  X  X  X
           X  X  X  X
     X  X  X  X  X  X  X     X
  ─────────────────────────────────────
   0  1  2  3  4  5  6  7  8  9 10 11
```

Line plot 5

```
              X
           X  X
           X  X
           X  X  X
           X  X  X     X
     X     X  X  X  X  X
     X     X  X  X  X  X
  ─────────────────────────────────────
   0  1  2  3  4  5  6  7  8  9 10 11
```

Line plot 6

```
              X
           X  X
           X  X
     X  X  X  X
     X  X  X  X
     X  X  X  X  X  X
     X  X  X  X  X  X
  ─────────────────────────────────────
   0  1  2  3  4  5  6  7  8  9 10 11
```

Which Data Are Made Up?

This is a discussion among three students trying to decide whether line plot C on Student Sheet 5 is real or made up. The teacher has stopped to ask how they are doing, but then probes only twice, first to redirect their thinking to properties of the actual distribution, and later to re-engage one student in the conversation.

```
Line plot C        X
                   X
                   X   X
               X   X   X
               X   X   X
               X   X   X
               X   X   X
               X   X   X
               X   X   X
               X   X   X
         ─────────────────────────────────
          0  1  2  3  4  5  6  7  8  9 10 11
```

Robby: Yu-Wei and I think that line plot C is made up, but Lindsay thinks it's true. I think it's not true because there are 6 line plots and 3 of them are gonna be true and 3 are gonna be false.

Lindsay: But you really think it's gonna go false, false, false, true, true, true?

Can you give me some reasons you think C is false, based on what we've learned by doing the experiment?

Yu-Wei: Because usually it doesn't start out at 4. It usually has at least a couple under 4 and there's too many 5's.

Lindsay: But it's possible for the lowest score to be 4.

Robby: All of this is possible, but it's not likely.

Lindsay: I think it's true because most of our data is around 4, 5, and 6 and a couple are around 7, and that's what they have here.

Robby: OK, Lindsay. Then listen to this question. *[Lindsay doesn't seem to be paying attention.]* Please listen. That's what the group is for. You think *that* many people would have gotten 5?

Lindsay: Yeah.

Robby: Why?

Lindsay: Because 5 is sort of what we expected. It's ¼ of 20, and that's what we expected people to get.

What do you think of that reasoning, Yu-Wei? The results *are* clustered around 5 where we would expect them to be, right?

Yu-Wei: Well, 5 is the most likely, but you're not likely to get that many. Don't you think you'd have someone get a 3? You got a 3, Lindsay.

Lindsay: But people aren't me.

Robby: But it could be just like your situation.

Lindsay: I guess so.

Robby: It's not really spread out enough, and don't you think at least some people would get 1, 2 or 3?

Lindsay: Yeah. And probably one would get 8 or 9, too.

The Scoring Options Game

Materials

- Transparency of Student Sheet 6, Game A (optional)
- Overhead projector and transparency (optional)
- Clear spinners (1 per pair)
- Student Sheet 6 (1 per pair)
- Student Sheet 7 (as needed, for challenge)
- Student Sheet 8 (1 per student, homework)

What Happens

Student pairs play a spinner game that reviews basic properties of numbers while the players apply what they've learned about probability in a game situation. They may, in the process, learn that selecting the most probable outcome does not guarantee success on a single trial. Student work focuses on:

- using knowledge of probabilities to select events most likely to occur
- learning to add probabilities of simple events

Activity

Learning the Game Strategy

Show an overhead transparency of Scoring Options, Game A (from Student Sheet 6), or copy the spinner template and the scoring options from that game onto the board.

Today you're going to play a game that involves both chance and skill. You and your partner will play cooperatively to get the best score you can. Together you'll have a spinner and a page that looks like this, with a spinner template *[point it out]* **and these scoring options** *[point]*. **To play the game, place your clear spinner on top of the template and spin. These options give six different ways that the player spinning can score a point.**

Read through the scoring options with the group, stopping to clarify rules and terminology as needed. Students may need to review the difference between a factor and a multiple. Examples work better than definitions to clarify these terms. You might say:

The *factors* **of 6 are 1, 6, 2, and 3. The** *multiples* **of 6 are 6, 12, 18, 24, and so on. They're the numbers you say when you count by 6. What are other multiples of 6?**

Leave examples of each term on the board so students can refer to them throughout the game.

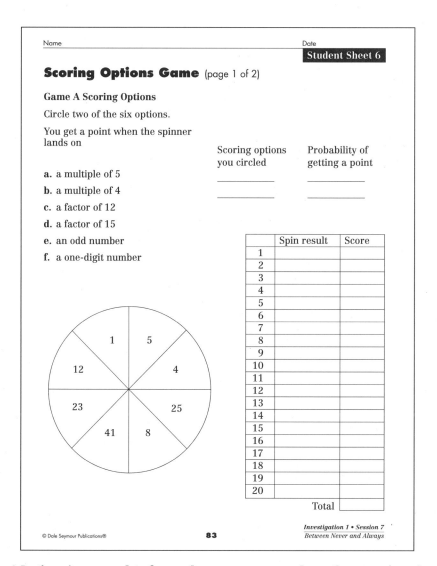

Scoring Options Game (page 1 of 2)

Game A Scoring Options

Circle two of the six options.

You get a point when the spinner lands on

	Scoring options you circled	Probability of getting a point
a. a multiple of 5	_____	_____
b. a multiple of 4	_____	_____
c. a factor of 12		
d. a factor of 15		
e. an odd number		
f. a one-digit number		

	Spin result	Score
1		
2		
3		
4		
5		
6		
7		
8		
9		
10		
11		
12		
13		
14		
15		
16		
17		
18		
19		
20		
	Total	

Let's spin a couple of rounds so you can see how the game works.

Use the template and a clear spinner. Spin once. Help students reason through each scoring option as it relates to the number that was spun. For example:

The spinner landed on 4. Is 4 a multiple of 5? No. Is 4 a multiple of 4? Yes. Then I'd score a point if I used that option. Let's keep going. Is 4 a factor of 12? Yes…

When students understand how to determine if a spin scores a point, explain the rest of the rules of the game:

Here's where strategy comes in. Before you begin playing the game, you and your partner will pick out two scoring options and circle them. You score a point only if the number you spin fits at least one of the options you circled.

For example, if one of your rules says, "You score a point when the spinner lands on an odd number," you'll get a point if the spinner lands on 41. If the spinner lands on a number that fits *both* of the scoring options you circled, you still get only one point. You may not switch options in the middle of the game.

In this game, you and your partner together are trying to get as many points as possible. You will spin 20 times in all. Before you choose your options, look at your template and the scoring options with your partner. Decide which are most likely to give you points. Once you've decided, but before you start spinning, write down the probability of getting a point using each rule.

You might demonstrate by asking the class to tell you the probability of spinning a factor of 12 with the spinner in Game A. (3⁄8)

Activity

Playing the Scoring Options Game

Distribute Student Sheet 6, with Games A and B, to each pair. Each should also have a clear spinner. Explain that as they finish Game A, they can go on to Game B, choosing options from the new set.

As pairs are playing the game, circulate and ask students to explain why they chose the scoring options they did.

Why did you pick these particular scoring options? Would you score any points with these other options? In a whole game (20 spins), how many points would you expect to score using your options?

Most students will recognize that they have more chances to win with some scoring options than with others. Encourage students to think through the possibilities in a numerical way by asking them to specify the probability of scoring a point. Suppose, for example, a student is considering option (a), a multiple of 5. If that student reasons, "That's a good option to pick because there are lots of multiples of 5 on the template," you might ask:

How many multiples of 5 are on the template? (2) Out of how many total possibilities? (8) What is the probability of landing on a multiple of 5? (2⁄8, or 1⁄4) How did you get 1⁄4?

Students should be able to explain that since the probabilities of 5 and 25 are each 1⁄8, the probability of one of those happening is 2⁄8, or 1⁄4. Continue asking students to explain how they determine the probabilities of various events as you question them about the advantages and disadvantages of the various scoring options.

Do you see any scoring option that gives you a greater probability of winning a point?

There are four versions of this game, two on Student Sheet 6 (Games A and B), and two more on Student Sheet 7 (Games C and D). For Game B, be sure students understand what is meant in option (e) by "a number whose digits add up to an even number."

Games C and D contain more challenging material. You may decide to omit these in your class, to assign them to particular student pairs who are ready for an extra challenge, or to make them available to everyone. If you decide to distribute the Student Sheet 7 challenge games, you may need to review the meanings of prime and square numbers.

Advise students to keep all their game records for a follow-up discussion.

How Did We Get the Highest Scores?

For this discussion, pick one of the games that everyone has played and determine the high scorers for the class. Invite this pair (referred to here as pair 1) to share the scoring options they picked and to explain why.

Select another pair (referred to here as pair 2) who used different scoring options for the same game, and have them explain why they chose the options they did. Then ask the class:

Which pair of scoring options do you think has the better probability of scoring a point on a single spin?

Some students may argue that pair 1, having the highest score, must have the scoring options with the highest probability. However, because of the nature of probability, it is possible to obtain the highest total without picking the options that are most likely to win points. After the students discuss their views, ask them to actually compute the probability of each scoring rule.

What is the probability of pair 1 scoring a point on one spin of the spinner?

Students work on this question with partners, then discuss as a class the answers they came up with, sharing how they computed the probability. There will likely be disagreements among students about how to determine these probabilities, in particular about how to deal with two scoring rules when some events are covered by both rules. See the **Teacher Note**, Probabilities of Composite Events (p. 45), for suggestions on how to facilitate this discussion.

What is the probability of pair 2 scoring a point on one spin of the spinner?

Do you see any pair of scoring options that gives you a greater probability of winning a point?

If several students picked the same scoring options, consider plotting their scores together on a line plot. Students can also play another round with the same scoring options to help them understand the variability they are likely to encounter from round to round.

Session 7 Follow-Up

🏠 **Homework**

Make Your Own Scoring Options   Distribute Student Sheet 8, Make Your Own Scoring Options, a blank version of the game played in class. At home, students make up their own scoring options and decide what numbers to put on the blank spinner template. The numbers should make sense, given the scoring options the students have created. Remind students to design the game so that some options are more likely to win than others.

After students have designed the game, they bring it to school and play it with a partner. Alternatively, students might play the game at home with an adult or a sibling. Briefly discuss how they can use a pencil and a paper clip as a makeshift spinner (holding the pencil, point down, in the very center of the template, and spinning a paper clip around the point).

Probabilities of Composite Events

The probabilities in the Scoring Options Game are complicated by the relationship between the two scoring rules a student chooses. In this game, a player scores a point when *either* of two rules is satisfied by the number on the spinner. To determine the probability of scoring a point with two particular rules, some students may compute the probability of getting a point with each rule, then add these two probabilities together.

This is a reasonable approach that will often result in the correct probability. For example, in Game A, this method works fine for determining the probability of scoring with option e, an odd number, and option b, a multiple of 4, as the two chosen rules. There are five odd numbers on the spinner (1, 5, 23, 25, 41) and three multiples of 4 (4, 8, 12). The probability of getting an odd number is 5/8 and the probability of getting a multiple of 4 is 3/8, and students can add 5/8 and 3/8 to get a probability of 8/8, or 1. In this case, by choosing these two rules, a player will always score a point no matter what number the spinner lands on. To check that this is true, we can see that every number on the spinner is either odd or a multiple of 4—so, indeed, every spin wins a point.

However, suppose students want to compute the probability of scoring a point by choosing option e, an odd number, and option f, a one-digit number. If they tried to compute this probability by adding 5/8 and 4/8 (since there are four one-digit numbers: 1, 4, 5, 8), they would get 9/8, which is more than 1 and therefore an impossible probability value.

What is the difference between these two situations? Why does adding probabilities work in one case and not in the other? In the first case, there is no intersection between the numbers that match each rule; no number on the spinner is both odd *and* a multiple of 4. In the second example, however, two numbers on the spinner fit both rules: 1 and 5 are both single-digit numbers and odd numbers. If we add 5/8 and 4/8 to get the probability of scoring a point, we are counting both 1 and 5 twice—and thus get an incorrect answer.

Some students may first realize there is a problem with the way they are dealing with the second set of rules when they discover they've computed a probability great than 1. You might motivate other stu-

dents to look again at the problem by asking whether these two options guarantee scoring a point on every spin. (The answer is no; they don't get a point when the spinner lands on 12, because it is neither odd or one digit.) To get the correct probability of scoring a point with options e and f, we must be careful not to count the same event more than once. The numbers that will score a point are the odd numbers 1, 5, 23, 25, 41 and the one-digit numbers *that we have not already counted:* 4 and 8. There are 7 numbers that will score a point, out of 8 on the spinner, so the probability is 7/8.

We often make a distinction in probability between *elementary* events and *composite* events. The elementary events in this case are the eight individual numbers on the spinner. They are elementary because we can't break them down into simpler events. The scoring rules give us composite events, which are made up of two or more elementary events. In this example from Game A, the composite event "an odd number" is made up of the elementary events {1, 5, 23, 25, 41}, and the composite event "a multiple of 5" is made up of the elementary events {5, 25}. The elementary events 5 and 25 are included in both composite events.

The more general point is that we can't always add the probabilities of two or more events occurring to get the probability of at least one of them occurring. We first have to make sure there is no overlap in the events.

In mathematics, this is often expressed like this: The probabilities of events can be added as long as the events are mutually exclusive. Events are mutually exclusive if no more than one of them can occur at the same time. When you flip a coin, the two possible events heads and tails are mutually exclusive because you can't get both of them on the same flip. With the spinner in Game A, "a multiple of 4" and "an odd number" are mutually exclusive because no multiple of 4 is an odd number. Because of this, you can determine the probability of getting one result or the other by adding together the separate probabilities. However, the events "a one-digit number" and "an odd number" are not mutually exclusive, so their probabilities cannot be added together to compute the probability that one or the other will occur.

Fair and Unfair Games

What Happens

Sessions 1 and 2: Rock, Paper, Scissors
Students play a three-person version of Rock, Paper, Scissors that is not fair—the players have different chances of winning. After collecting data that seem to show the game is unfair, students enumerate all possible ways for each player to win and discover that it is indeed unfair. Groups then modify the rules of the game to make it fair.

Session 3: Does a Fair Game Always Look Fair? Students make and share lists of games that involve chance only, skill only, and a combination of the two. They discuss any differences of opinion about how the games are classified. A new game, Race to the Top, is introduced; it is played with a one-half spinner that students know is fair. The class results are used to prompt a discussion of what it means for a game to be fair.

Sessions 4 and 5: The Unfair Spinner Game
Students report on the methods used by three different generations for deciding who goes first. They discuss the fairness of the various methods. Then, after playing a spinner game that is clearly unfair, groups modify the rules to make the game fair. After each group writes up rules for their game, students play the games designed by other groups and decide whether they agree that the games are fair.

Mathematical Emphasis

- Interpreting fairness of a game as equal probability of winning
- Developing systematic ways to generate a list that includes all the ways an event can occur
- Applying knowledge of probability to design a fair game
- Analyzing the fairness of games
- Distinguishing between games of chance and games of skill
- Interpreting data represented on line plots
- Analyzing group data in terms of general features such as center and spread
- Understanding variability in the results of fair games

What to Plan Ahead of Time

Materials

- Chart paper (Sessions 1–2 and 4–5)
- Clear spinners: 1 per pair (Sessions 3–5)
- One-half spinner templates from Investigation 1: 1 per pair (Session 3)
- Overhead projector (Sessions 3–5, optional)
- Pennies or other coins to flip: 1 per group (Sessions 4–5)

Other Preparation

- Duplicate student sheets and teaching resources (located at the end of this unit) in the following quantities. If you have Student Activity Booklets, copy only the item marked with an asterisk.

For Sessions 1–2

Student Sheet 9, Games of Skill and Chance (p. 91): 1 per student (homework)

For Session 3

Student Sheet 10, Race to the Top Score Sheet (p. 92): 1 per pair

Student Sheet 11, Deciding Who Goes First (p. 93): 1 per student (homework)

For Sessions 4–5

Student Sheet 12, Assigning Household Jobs (p. 94): 1 per student (homework)

Unfair Spinner Game Templates* (p. 95): 1 per group of 4, cut apart to make two spinners

- Make two demonstration spinners from the Unfair Spinner Game Templates (p. 95). (Sessions 4–5)

Rock, Paper, Scissors

Materials

- Chart paper
- Student Sheet 9 (1 per student, homework)

What Happens

Students play a three-person version of Rock, Paper, Scissors that is not fair—the players have different chances of winning. After collecting data that seem to show the game is unfair, students enumerate all possible ways for each player to win and discover that it is indeed unfair. Groups then modify the rules of the game to make it fair. Student work focuses on:

- interpreting fairness of a game as equal probability of winning
- developing systematic ways to generate a list that includes all the ways an event can occur
- analyzing the fairness of games
- applying knowledge of probability to design a fair game

Ten-Minute Math: Nearest Answer Continue to do the Nearest Answer activity once or twice in the next few days. You might try some number line problems, for example:

8	A		10	A is nearest:
└──	─┴──	─────	──┘	8.1 8.5 9 9.25

Select problems from the examples provided on p. 71, or design your own. For full directions and variations on this activity, see p. 71.

Activity

What Makes a Game Unfair?

Many students will already know the game Rock, Paper, Scissors (perhaps by another name). Briefly review the rules for any who may not know them.

❖ **Tip for the Linguistically Diverse Classroom** Have an actual rock, sheet of paper, and scissors at hand as you explain the rules. This will help everyone associate the hand gestures with the three objects.

Rock, Paper, Scissors (Traditional Game) The traditional game is played in pairs. For each round, players recite in unison, "Rock, paper, scissors, shoot!" As they say "shoot," each player simultaneously makes one of three symbolic hand shapes: a fist (rock), a flat hand (paper), or a spread index finger and middle finger (scissors).

When the hand shapes made by the two players are rock and scissors, rock wins (rock crushes scissors). When the hand shapes made are paper and rock, paper wins (paper covers rock). And when the hand shapes are scissors and paper, scissors wins (scissors cut paper). When players make the same hand shape, no one wins and that round doesn't count.

Rock   Paper   Scissors

Ask for volunteers to demonstrate the original game. After they have played it a few times, ask:

Is this game fair? Does each player have the same chance of winning on each turn? Is there one hand shape that gives you a better chance of winning?

Rock, Paper, Scissors (3-Player Version)   After students have discussed whether the original game is fair, introduce the rules of a different version of the game for groups of three players. A group consists of player A, player B, and player C—roles that are randomly assigned. After the chant, "Rock, paper, scissors, shoot!" each player simultaneously makes a hand shape (rock, paper, or scissors).

The rules for deciding who wins on each turn are different for this game:

■ **If all three players make the same hand shape, player A gets a point.**

■ **If all three players make different hand shapes, player B gets a point.**

■ **If two players make the same hand shape and one makes a different shape, player C gets a point.**

Write the rules on chart paper so that students can refer to them throughout this session.

Rock, Paper, Scissors   —   3-Player Version
• All three the same: 1 point for Player A
• All three different: 1 point for Player B
• Two the same, one different: 1 point for Player C

Demonstrate a few rounds of play. To set the stage for the later discussion about the fairness of the game, ask whether players feel they have equal chances to win.

If you wanted to win the game, which player would you rather be, or does it matter?

Forming Groups   Here and elsewhere in this investigation, consider forming groups by drawing students' names out of a container. This method lends itself to further discussion of probability. For each group of three, the first name chosen becomes player A, the second name, player B, and the third, player C. Before picking the first name, ask:

What are the chances I'll draw your name out?

Repeat the question as you pick the next card, and the next. As the number of names in the container decreases, the probability that you will pick the name of any one particular student who has not yet been chosen goes up. For example, if you have 30 students in the class, the probability will go from 1 out of 30 to 1 out of 29 to 1 out of 28, and so on.

Playing the Game   Students play the game for 20 rounds. Ask them to record their results in a way that ensures they don't go over 20 rounds.

When groups are finished playing, collect the scores on the board. Arrange the scores so it is possible to tally up class points for player A, for player B, and for player C. For example, you might organize this information in a chart.

| Number of Wins | | |
Player A	Player B	Player C
Group 1 — 1	5	14
Group 2 — 3	6	11
Group 3 — 4	5	11
Group 4 — 3	2	15
Group 5 — 4	4	12
Group 6 — 2	4	14
Total wins 26	44	130

Discussing the Results   After the class results have been tallied, discuss what the results suggest about the fairness of the three-person game, and the reasons why it's not fair.

Is one player more likely to win? If you wanted to win, which player would you choose to be? Is this game fair or unfair?

It will become very clear by looking at the results that player C has an unfair advantage. Challenge the class to figure out why. Someone will probably suggest that there are more ways for player C to get a point. With your class, chart all the ways for each player to earn a point. Begin by listing all the ways player A can get a point (there are three). It may be easiest to keep track on a three-column chart, using the player names as headings:

Ways Player A Can Win

	Player A	Player B	Player C
1	rock	rock	rock
2	paper	paper	paper
3	scissors	scissors	scissors

Next, determine all the ways player B can get a point (there are six). Ask the students to name the various possibilities, writing them on the board in the order they give them to you. When the students can name no other possibilities, ask:

Are you sure there are no other possibilities?

Encourage students to think of systematic ways of listing the possibilities so that they can be sure all of them are accounted for. For example, in the chart below, all combinations that involve player A choosing rock are listed, then all combinations in which player A chooses paper, and so on.

Ways Player B Can Win

	Player A	Player B	Player C
1	rock	paper	scissors
2	rock	scissors	paper
3	paper	rock	scissors
4	paper	scissors	rock
5	scissors	rock	paper
6	scissors	paper	rock

Since player C has the greatest number of ways to win, work on these combinations last (there are 18 of them). This time, students first work in their groups to organize a list of possibilities that give a point to player C. Encourage them to find a systematic way of generating all the possibilities.

Ways Player C Can Win

	Player A	Player B	Player C
1	rock	rock	paper
2	rock	rock	scissors
3	rock	scissors	rock
4	rock	paper	rock
5	paper	rock	rock
6	scissors	rock	rock
7	scissors	scissors	rock
8	scissors	scissors	paper
9	scissors	paper	scissors
10	scissors	rock	scissors
11	rock	scissors	scissors
12	paper	scissors	scissors
13	paper	paper	scissors
14	paper	paper	rock
15	paper	rock	paper
16	paper	scissors	paper
17	scissors	paper	paper
18	rock	paper	paper

Activity

Making the Game Fair

Working in groups, students figure out how to change the three-player version of Rock, Paper, Scissors to make it a fair game. Although they must keep it a three-person game and maintain a rock-paper-scissors component, students may change any of the other rules. They write down the rules for their new game and include an explanation of why it is fair.

Before groups begin working, make sure students understand what you mean by a fair game.

Let's assume you want to win. If the game is fair, you won't care whether you are player A, player B, or player C. Each player in a fair game has an equal chance of winning.

For further discussion of what's involved in determining fairness, see the **Teacher Note,** What's Fair? (p. 55).

While students are working on their new rules, walk around the room and observe them. You may find that although every group can adjust the game to make it fairer, some groups will not get it exactly fair. Challenge these students to evaluate their rules further.

How could you prove to someone that your game is truly fair? How do you know each player has an equal chance of winning?

In the next activity, students will get a chance to play again with their new rules. The scores from these rounds of play will give some indication of whether the students' adjusted game is now fair.

Playing New Versions of the Game

Students begin by playing 20 rounds of their own version of the game. Then they share with other groups how they modified the game. During the next two sessions, students will be designing more fair games. It is important to give them a chance now to critique and learn from each other's solutions. See the **Dialogue Box,** Discussing Students' New Game Rules (p. 56), for an example of one group's discussion of a new game.

If you're not sure that another group's solution is fair, keep asking questions until one of you has convinced the other.

Some students may offer their scores after playing the new game as proof that the game is fair. Others, who have indeed created fair new rules, might say, "We thought it was fair, but it didn't work out evenly when we played it, so it must not be fair." The next session (Does a Fair Game Always Look Fair?) addresses this issue. In the meantime, you might ask:

Are your results proof that the game is now fair? Could you get these scores even if the game were unfair?

There are many ways to organize the sharing of solutions; following are some possibilities.

1. Groups pair up. Each group explains their rules and plays a few rounds of their game with members of the other group. They then discuss whether that game is fair.

2. Each group writes their rules on an overhead transparency. They display the rules and take a few minutes to explain them to the class. Allow time for other students to ask questions or to comment. Ask the class to determine whether or not they think the solution is fair and to explain why.

3. As groups finish, assign half of them to remain at their seats and demonstrate their revised games to their classmates. The rest of the class walks from group to group and listens to the explanation of each new game. They discuss whether or not each game is fair.

4. Students write complete directions for how to play the game. These directions are placed around the room. Groups rotate around the room, thinking about and playing as many games as possible. Put a pad of stick-on notes at each game station so that students can post questions or comments they have about each game. Spend a few minutes at the end of class discussing games that students think may not be fair. Use their comments on the stick-on notes to launch the discussion.

❖ **Tip for the Linguistically Diverse Classroom** Choice 3 above is best suited to classrooms with limited-English proficient students.

Sessions 1 and 2 Follow-Up

 **Homework**

Games of Skill and Chance   Distribute Student Sheet 9, Games of Skill and Chance. Students brainstorm lists of games they know that are based on skill, games that are based on chance, and games that involve a combination of skill and chance. If your students' backgrounds are diverse, encourage them to include games that are played in their families or communities, even if those games are not well known to others in the class. Remind students to bring their lists back to class.

❖ **Tip for the Linguistically Diverse Classroom** Before making this assignment, clarify the difference between games of skill and games of chance with some models. Demonstrate and let students participate in quick activities that take skill to win (such as shooting paper balls at the wastebasket), and some that are won by chance (such as rolling a number cube for the highest number).

What's Fair?

The everyday meaning of the word *fair* is not quite the same as its meaning in probability. We typically use the word to indicate that something is just or equitable. In the spirit of fairness, we learn to take turns, alternate who does the dishes, and make our portions of ice cream as even as possible.

In a homework assignment (Student Sheet 12, Assigning Household Jobs), students will see what would happen if they assigned household chores by drawing names randomly out of a container. They discover that this doesn't usually lead to an equal distribution of jobs and that often one person would be doing dishes several nights in a row. This is not fair in the ordinary sense of the word because it's not equitable. But it *is* fair in another sense: There is no bias or favoritism in the assignment of jobs because everyone has an equal chance of being chosen.

This is what we mean when we say a game is fair. We mean that there is no bias in the rules that favors one player over the others. This does not mean, however, that each person will win equally often, or that the person who wins this time will lose the next, as if the players were taking turns winning. Thus, fairness in this mathematical sense is established through a logical analysis—looking at the rules—more than by looking at the results.

Sometimes it's easy to determine whether a game is fair. Young children figure out that using "Eenie, meenie, minie, mo" to choose one out of a group is not fair, since the person selected can be determined beforehand by choosing where to begin the count. If in the random assignment of household jobs there were two slips of paper with the child's name on it, but only one slip for each of the other family members, everyone would know this was unfair even before looking at the results.

For many games, determining fairness is not so simple. Some students may be tempted to think that if a game is fair, each player would win equally often. However, if we flip a fair coin 20 times, we will probably not end up with an even split between heads and tails. Sometimes we won't get even close to an even split. Likewise, even in fair games, somebody wins each game, sometimes by a lot, and that same person may win again if we play the game again.

Playing a game over and over can sometimes help us figure out if the game is fair. If the game is grossly unfair, the results over several games will probably be quite uneven, and will continue that way over more and more games. The three-person version of Rock, Paper, Scissors is so unfair that in every group, player C will probably win more than A and B. Also, playing the game makes us more aware of how the game works, and we can discover subtle biases in the rules that we didn't notice at first. As students determine who wins each round of the three-person version of Rock, Paper, Scissors, they become aware of the different outcomes of the game, and see that the majority of the outcomes favor player C.

An important lesson is that while results from playing a game may lead us to question the game's fairness, the way to be sure is to analyze the structure of the game (the rules and the physical devices being used) in search of bias. Asking students whether a game is fair before they play it can help focus attention on the rules as opposed to the results. The arguments students make for fairness before playing their new game will have to be based on analysis of their rules. Remind them that if they believe the rules are fair, they won't care which player they are.

Discussing Students' New Game Rules

Our Game

Number the page 1-18. Write 1-A, 2-B, 3-C, 4-A, 5-B, etc. Play the game the same way. If you are on a A # and you get all the same, A gets a point. If you are on a B# and you get all different then B gets a point. If on a C# and you get two the same, one different, then C gets a point. You only win on a number with your letter.

For the class discussion of the students' revised rules for Rock, Paper, Scissors (p. 53), three students (Alani, Jeff, and Toshi) have the rules they designed visible on an overhead. After the group summarizes their rules, the other students begin asking questions.

Marcus: I don't understand. Like, if I'm player A, how do I win a point?

Alani: If you're player A? Well, the first thing is that you can only win on round 1, 4, 7... any round that has been given your letter. But then to win, you have to have all three players come up with the same thing on that round—like all three come up rock, just like before.

Marcus: OK. So it's the same rules as before, but you can only win...

Jeff: Yeah, on rounds that have been given your letter.

Marcus: But why is that fair now?

Jeff: Well, you all have the same number of rounds you can win on, so the chance is $1/3$ of winning.

Amy Lynn: I don't think it's fair because C will come up more often. It's still the same rules. If C comes up more often with the original rules, it will come up more often this way, too.

Continued on next page

Toshi: We discussed that when we were making it up, but A, B, and C have the same amount of chances.

Amy Lynn: If C comes up more often, how do they have the same chances?

What is it you mean, Toshi, by saying A, B and C have the same amount of chances?

Toshi: Everyone can win only on their turn, and when we played it the scores came out about the same for each of us.

Amy Lynn: I still don't think it's fair.

Jeff: There's no way to make this game totally fair. All games are basically chance, and sometimes everyone will win the same amount, and other times different. So no game is totally fair.

It's true that even games we call fair games don't guarantee that each player will win the same number of times. The question Amy Lynn is raising, however, is whether one of the players still has an advantage. One way to see if

you believe the game is fair in this sense is to ask yourself: If I could choose before the game started, which player would I choose to be, or would it matter?

Amy Lynn: I'd still want to be C. When C is on his row, he has—what did we get when we figured all the ways?

Duc: There's 18 ways.

Amy Lynn: Right, 18 different ways he can win. But when A is on a line, there are only 3 ways to win. So I agree with Marcus that the game is really the same as it was before—it's still unfair.

Jeff appears to be using the common sense of the term *fair* to argue that games based on chance tend not to result in even divisions of wins and losses—and he is correct. This is an important point about chance, but does not acknowledge the mathematical sense of fairness. The teacher chooses to emphasize the point Jeff makes, and then to focus attention on whether the rules give one of the players an unfair advantage.

Does a Fair Game Always Look Fair?

Materials

- Completed Student Sheet 9 (from homework)
- Clear spinners (1 per pair)
- One-half templates (1 per pair)
- Student Sheet 10 (1 per pair)
- Student Sheet 11 (1 per student, homework)
- Overhead projector (optional)

What Happens

Students make and share lists of games that involve chance only, skill only, and a combination of the two. They discuss any differences of opinion about how the games are classified. A new game, Race to the Top, is introduced; it is played with a one-half spinner that students know is fair. The class results are used to prompt a discussion of what it means for a game to be fair. Student work focuses on:

- distinguishing between games of chance and games of skill
- interpreting data represented on line plots
- analyzing group data in terms of general features such as center and spread
- understanding variability in the results of fair games

Activity

Games of Skill, Games of Chance

Divide students into groups of four to discuss the homework, their completed Student Sheet 9. If students have listed games that their classmates don't know, encourage them to explain the rules to the class.

Share your lists of games with the others in your group. Be sure to describe any games that people in the group don't know. Keep track of different points of view that arise about where to list the games. We will discuss these as a class.

After about 5 minutes, bring the class together to discuss any disagreements about where to place the games. For students who have trouble defining a game of chance, you might ask:

If you played the game with a younger brother or sister, would you both have an equal chance of winning?

Then ask students to look for similarities among the games of chance.

What, if anything, do the games of chance have in common? (Often, they involve number cubes, spinners, or cards.)

Student pairs play the game Race to the Top, using a one-half spinner (a clear spinner with the same one-half template used in Investigation 1). Distribute Student Sheet 10, Race to the Top Score Sheet, and explain the rules of the game.

A Fair Game: Race to the Top

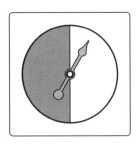

You and your partner first decide who will be player A and who will be player B. Take turns spinning. Player A gets a point if the spinner lands on green. Player B gets a point if the spinner lands on white. You get a point whenever the spinner lands on your color, no matter who is spinning on that turn.

When you get a point, put an X on the grid on the Race to the Top Score Sheet. Start at the bottom of the grid and work your way up. The player who reaches the top of the column first wins the round. When one of you wins, begin a new round on a new grid. Play six times, until you've used all the grids on the score sheet. At the end of six rounds, count up how many rounds each player won.

Although this activity is similar to spinning on the one-half template in Investigation 1, Session 3, the focus is now on what the distribution of results of a fair game can look like. We have found that students think differently about the results of spinning when they are just recording data and when they are playing a game. When they are playing a game, it is much more bothersome when the outcomes of the spinner don't divide evenly.

After you explain the rules, but before students begin playing, ask:

Is this a fair game? What is the probability of player A winning a round? What is the probability of player B winning a round? If they play six rounds, how many do you think each player will win?

What makes the game fair? If you wanted to win the game, would you care whether you were player A or player B?

Class Results from Race to the Top

On the board or overhead, draw a line plot with a range from 0 to 6. Go around the room, asking each pair to report the number of rounds won by player A. Use either X's or students' initials to represent their results on the line plot. Alternatively, you could have groups come up after they have finished playing the game and put their results on the line plot.

A line plot for 15 pairs of students might look like this:

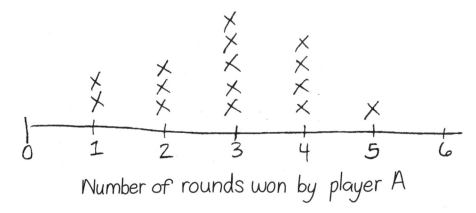

Draw another line plot and collect the results for player B in the same way. If students notice that the two line plots are mirror images of one another, explore with them why this is so.

One player may win five rounds and the other only one. (The probability of this happening is about 1/5.) It is likely that this result will occur for at least one pair in your class. In most cases, 3 will be the center (median) of the line plot. Many other distributions can occur, so don't be surprised if the distribution you get looks quite different from this one. The **Teacher Note,** What to Expect from the Fair Version of Race to the Top (p. 62) shows some of the variety you might see in your class. The main point is that, even with a fair game, it is not unusual for one player to win more often than the other.

Discuss the class line plots with your students. Begin by making sure students understand what each X represents. Then go on to discuss the distribution of results.

Which X represents *your* results? What does three X's over the 2 show us?

Did each player win exactly half the time? But we said this game was fair. How do you explain these results?

As with Rock, Paper, Scissors, students may be tempted to conclude that a game is unfair or that something was wrong with the spinner when results don't divide evenly. Examining the results of a game that is clearly fair can help students understand that even in a fair game, we don't expect the results always to come out even. There is variability in the results due to chance. The **Dialogue Box,** Bad Breaks in Fair Games (p. 63), illustrates some things you might hear from students during this discussion.

Session 3 Follow-Up

Deciding Who Goes First   Distribute Student Sheet 11, Deciding Who Goes First. Students compile information from three generations, if possible. Go over the directions with students before they leave, and remind them to bring this sheet back to class for discussion in the next session.

 **Homework**

❖ **Tip for the Linguistically Diverse Classroom**   To ensure understanding of the task, ask students to model several ways they decide who goes first. Then sketch a family tree on the board showing three generations—children, parents, and grandparents. Explain that students will ask this question to family members or other people representing two older generations. Students can write their responses on Student Sheet 11 in their primary language or give their answers orally in class discussion during the next session.

Making Line Plots of Their Own Results   Students may continue to play Race to the Top, making their own scoring grids on notebook paper. Each pair then makes a line plot of their results and adds those results to the class line plot.

 **Extensions**

Playing a Game from a Different Culture   After reading over the games of chance that students listed on Student Sheet 9, select one or two that are likely to be unfamiliar to many in the class. Have the student who listed the game explain how to play it. If the game is suitable for class use, students may play it in small groups and discuss whether it is a fair game.

What to Expect from the Fair Version of Race to the Top

The computer simulations of Race to the Top shown in the chart give you some idea of the results you might expect to see in your class. We assumed 30 students in a class—15 pairs—playing six rounds of the game as indicated in the activity. We did the simulation ten times to show what the results might look like in ten different classes.

The amount of variation from class to class is striking. However, the median number of wins for player A is 3 in all but one case (in class 10, the median is 2). The results also suggest that in a class with 15 pairs playing, it is very likely that more than one group will end up with a 1–5 split. This is true even if only 10 pairs are playing, although the fewer pairs playing, the harder it will be to get at least one extreme result (one player winning only 1 or 0 games out of the 6).

If we repeated this simulation many times, we'd find that roughly 30 percent of the students would split evenly; about 45 percent would divide 4–2 (including 4–2 and 2–4 together); about 20 percent would divide 5–1; and about 4 percent would divide 6–0.

Number of wins for player A

	0	1	2	3	4	5	6
Class 1	0	0	4	4	4	3	0
Class 2	0	1	6	2	3	3	0
Class 3	0	2	5	3	2	2	1
Class 4	0	3	2	4	3	3	0
Class 5	0	1	1	7	3	3	0
Class 6	0	1	2	8	3	1	0
Class 7	0	3	2	6	3	1	0
Class 8	0	1	6	1	4	3	0
Class 9	1	1	5	5	1	1	1
Class 10	0	1	7	7	0	0	0

Bad Breaks in Fair Games

Two students are discussing their results as they play Race to the Top with the one-half spinner.

Christine: There's something wrong with this spinner. You can't get white that many times in a row.

Desiree: Yes you can. It's a game of chance.

[Two minutes later...]

Christine: This spinner isn't fair. Desiree won five games and I only won one.

Well, people are beginning to put their results up on the board. Why don't you put yours up and see how it compares to what others got?

Christine: I think it's weird that you can get white so may times in a row.

[Whispering] **Well guess what? You can. That's why we're doing this. And I was worried that no one would get results like yours, so I'm really glad you did.**

The class begins discussing the results after all the groups have put their data on the board (see their line plots, below).

Look at the data for the class. What do you notice?

Corey: Most people won three games.

Antonio: It's a fair game. It's in the middle. Player A won three games and B won three, mostly.

Christine: Desiree and I were the outliers. I won only one game, and I thought it was unfair because we would get like six white in a row and no greens, then two greens and a lot of whites. I thought something was wrong with the spinner.

Kevin: Maybe it was how you spun it.

Sofia: I think maybe it is in favor of green (player A) because when you color the spinner there's maybe a lot of bumps on the green so that slows the spinner down there.

Greg: But Christine *was* green.

When a game is fair, does it mean each player always wins half the time?

Desiree: No. If it's a game of pure chance, it's fair. If we played it again, we would probably get different results. Maybe the next time I would win only once, but that wouldn't mean the game wasn't fair.

The teacher helped Christine cope with the disappointment of losing by letting her know that she expected that someone in the class would get very uneven results. It's fine that students challenge the fairness of the spinner. The idea that coloring one side of the spinner might produce a bias is sophisticated reasoning, and describes something that could well happen. However, the more important point for students to consider is that uneven results in this case can occur purely by chance.

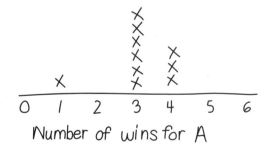

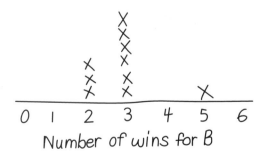

The Unfair Spinner Game

What Happens

Students report on the methods used by three different generations for deciding who goes first. They discuss the fairness of the various methods. Then, after playing a spinner game that is clearly unfair, groups modify the rules to make the game fair. After each group writes up rules for their game, students play the games designed by other groups and decide whether they agree that the games are fair. Student work focuses on:

- interpreting fairness of a game as equal probability of winning
- analyzing the fairness of games

Materials

- Chart paper
- Completed Student Sheet 11 (from homework)
- Demonstration spinners (two versions of unfair spinners)
- Clear spinners (2 per group of 4)
- Unfair Spinner Game Templates (1 of each spinner per group of 4)
- Pennies or other coins to flip (1 per group)
- Student Sheet 12 (1 per student, homework)
- Overhead projector (optional)

Activity

Who Goes First: What's Fair?

Spend about 10 minutes on this activity, which is a follow-up to the home-work assignment at the end of Session 3.

Make a chart with three headings: My Generation, One Generation Back, and Two Generations Back. Compile the data students have collected.

My Generation	One Generation Back	Two Generations Back
Roll a number cube	Pick a name out of hat	Draw straws
Flip coins	1-2-3 shoot	1-potato, 2-potato
Spinner	Stack up hands on a baseball bat	Eenie meenie minie mo

Encourage students to explain any methods of deciding who goes first that are unfamiliar to others in the class. This activity is rich with potential for cross-generational and cross-cultural sharing.

For the next couple of minutes, talk with a neighbor about which of these ways you think are fair. Why do you think they're fair?

Bring the group back together. Mark in some way all the methods that the class agrees are fair. Suggest that students try out some of these in the future as a classroom or playground procedure.

Playing the Unfair Spinner Game

Introduce the Unfair Spinner Game, which students will play in groups of four. Distribute the Unfair Spinner Game Templates, giving each group both Spinner 1 and Spinner 2. Each group is divided into two teams who will be spinning simultaneously.

Hold up your demonstration spinners and explore the differences between the two templates.

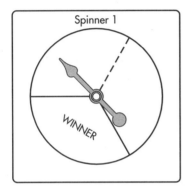 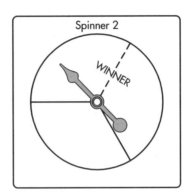

In this game, your pair gets a point if your spinner lands on the section that is labeled "winner." What are the chances of winning if you have Spinner 1? (1 out of 3) **What are the chances of winning if you have Spinner 2?** (2 out of 3) **Would you rather get Spinner 1 or Spinner 2?**

Flip a coin to decide who gets to choose the spinner they will use. Flip the coin just once, and have a member of the other pair call it before it lands. If the call is correct, that pair gets to select which spinner they play with. If the call is incorrect, your pair gets to choose its spinner.

Once each pair has a spinner, both pairs spin them at the same moment. Your pair wins a point only if you land on the "winner" section of your own spinner. Both pairs could win a point in the same round if their spinners landed on "winner." Keep track of your points. The object of the game is to be the first team to get ten points.

Supply a coin to each group of four; they flip it to determine which team gets their choice of spinner. Students play this version just long enough to understand the rules. As students are playing, circulate around the room and check to see that everyone is clear on the rules. Most groups will not finish playing this version of the game. Stop the class after about 5 minutes and ask:

Is this a fair game?

After a brief discussion, tell students they will spend the remainder of the period changing the rules to make a game that *is* fair.

Activity

Designing a Fair Game with Unfair Spinners

You will work with your group of four to make this spinner game fair. When you play your new version, you'll again flip a coin to find out which pair gets its choice of spinner. Remember, if it's really a fair game, you won't need to worry about which spinner you end up with. The chances of winning will be equal with either spinner.

To make the game fair, students must work within the following constraints. Copy the list where everybody can see it.

- You cannot change either spinner.
- Once pairs have flipped a coin at the beginning of the game to determine who gets which spinner, the pairs can't trade spinners. If a pair gets Spinner 1, they must keep it for the whole game.
- Pairs can get points only by landing on the "winner" section of their own spinner.
- The game should take at least 2 minutes, but no more than 5 minutes, to play.

What kinds of rules could you change in order to make this game fair? Let's focus on the types of things you might think about changing, not the details of the rules. You'll work those out with your group of four.

Brainstorm a list on the board or overhead, being open to all ideas. Your list might include:

- the number of points each pair gets on a winning spin
- the number of times each pair gets to spin
- whether one pair spins many times and then the other pair spins, or they spin simultaneously
- the total number of spins in the game
- the number of points needed to win the game
- added twists about how pairs get points

As students are creating their rules for fair games, circulate and ask groups how they know their game is now fair. This is the time to challenge the groups to rethink their reasoning if you believe the game is still unfair. The groups should be playing short versions of their games as they design them to help them think about the fairness of the rules.

When you play with your new rules, does each pair have an equal chance to win? If your pair got to select a spinner first, which one would you select? Why?

Writing Up New Rules   Once groups are satisfied that their rules turn the Unfair Spinner Game into a Fair Spinner Game, each member of the group writes out complete directions.

Later, you'll play some of the games that other groups have designed, and they'll play yours. So you need to write a set of instructions that your classmates can follow. I want each member of your group to write out a set of instructions. On the same page, write a brief explanation of why you think the game is now fair.

❖ **Tip for the Linguistically Diverse Classroom**   Students who are not writing comfortably in English might use drawings of the spinners to help them explain the new rules.

Students will probably need about 10 minutes to complete this task. When they have finished their individual work, have them come together again in their groups of four.

As a group, look over what each person has written. Then work together on one set of instructions that you think will allow another group to play your game without asking you any questions. Be sure to include instructions on how to win or end the game. Also agree on a brief explanation of why you think the game is now fair, and add that to the end of your directions.

In the next activity, students will move around the room playing each other's games. For this to work efficiently, each group will need two copies of their rules—one for each pair. If possible, plan on copying a set for each group, or ask students to write out two complete versions.

Person with greater chance must land on WINNER twice to equal one point.

Spinner 1 has to get 5 and Spinner 2 has to get 10 in the same amount of time.

Assessment

Judging the Fairness of Games

Each group of four now breaks into two teams to share their new game with their classmates. They flip a coin to see which pair is the "home" team and which is the "away" team. The home team stays where they are; the away team goes to another group. Both teams need their own copy of their group's game rules.

As you join in new groups, exchange copies of your rules. You should each be able to learn how to play the other's game by reading these directions. When you've finished reading and cleared up any questions, play a few rounds of both your games.

Students continue in this way, moving around the room and playing other games that their classmates designed. They play as many different versions as time allows.

Allow 5–10 minutes for students to complete the following assessment task:

Choose one of the new games you played today, and write a brief explanation of whether you think the game is now fair. Be sure to give reasons for why you think it's fair or not.

Be sure students understand that they are not to select their own group's game to write about.

❖ **Tip for the Linguistically Diverse Classroom** Offer students a visual rating system to indicate their opinion of the fairness of a game (for example, ☆☆☆ = 100 percent fair, ☆☆ = somewhat fair, ◯ = unfair). To complete the assessment, they might give their explanations to you orally, using the spinners as visual aids.

In this assessment you are not expected to determine yourself whether or not any particular game is indeed fair; rather, you focus on each student's analysis of a game's fairness. In assessing students' understanding, you should look for arguments that are not based solely on the results of playing the game. For example, students should mention any rules that give one player an advantage over the other and should be able to explain this advantage in terms of a higher probability of winning.

For some examples of the type of reasoning to expect, refer to the **Dialogue Box,** Discussing Students' New Game Rules (p. 56). While talking about their revised rules for the three-player Rock, Paper, Scissors game, the students in that sample dialogue not only focus on actual results but also analyze the game in terms of probability.

Choosing Student Work to Save

As the unit ends, you may want to select one of the following options for creating a record of students' work on this unit.

■ Students look back through their folders or notebooks and write about what they learned in this unit, what they remember most, and what was hard or easy for them. Students might complete this work during their writing time.

■ Students select one or two pieces of their work as their best, and you also choose one or two pieces of their work to be saved. This work is saved in a portfolio for the year. You might include students' written responses to the assessment Judging the Fairness of Games (p. 68). Students can create a separate page with brief comments describing each piece of work.

■ You may want to send a selection of work home for families to see. Students write cover letters, describing their work in this unit. This work should be returned if you are keeping a year-long portfolio of mathematics work for each student.

Sessions 4 and 5 Follow-Up

 **Homework**

Assigning Household Jobs   After Session 4, distribute Student Sheet 12, Assigning Household Jobs. Discuss the assignment with the students, perhaps giving an example from your own household. Point out that students will be simulating a month of chores by drawing names for each "day." Ask students if they think this approach will be fair, but hold most discussion until the follow-up (see Extension).

❖ **Tip for the Linguistically Diverse Classroom** Model the activity with slips of paper and a container. Demonstrate a recordkeeping system. Students might respond to the fairness question in their primary language.

For Christine's discussion of her results (below), see the next page.

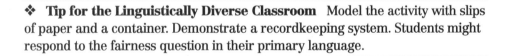

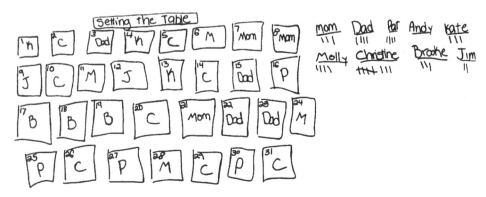

Discussing the Household Jobs Homework Choose a couple of unusual results to share with the class. Here is one possible question for discussion: Is it fair to use a random method of assigning jobs?

Some students will argue that it isn't fair because some family members would do less, while others would do more. Other students may counter that the method of selecting is still fair because everyone had the same chance of ending up with a heavy (or light) load. This again gets into the difference between the everyday meaning and the mathematical meaning of fairness, as discussed in the **Teacher Note,** What's Fair? (p. 55). By asking appropriate questions, you can help students focus on this difference.

I don't think this method is fair because in a big family like mine there is a big chance that one person is going to be left out and won't have to do that chore.

It would be less fair in a year because I (Christine) might end up setting the table 80 times while Andy might never or very few times. My parents always make the kids do the dishes anyway. Here is a more fair way to do it.

Monday - Pat
Tuesday - Andy
Wednesday - Kate
Thursday - Jim
Friday - Molly
Saturday - Christine
Sunday - Brooke

A kid will set the table 1 day each week.

Nearest Answer

Basic Activity

Students estimate answers to computation problems by rounding numbers in the problems and computing mentally. They pick the closest answer among the choices that are provided. In a variation, students choose an approximate number for a place marked on a number line between two given numbered points.

Nearest Answer provides practice with rounding numbers and estimating answers. This kind of thinking helps in checking answers found by calculator. Students' work focuses on:

- rounding numbers
- calculating mentally
- comparing possible answers to find the closest one

Materials

- Overhead projector
- Overhead transparencies of the problems you will use in the session; choose from the examples in the discussion that follows, or design similar problems yourself.
- Pieces of paper or cardboard for covering parts of the problems
- Calculators (optional)

Procedure

Step 1. Prepare a problem and four answer choices. Keep it hidden from the students. If you are writing your own, include as one answer a fairly round number that is a good estimate, and three other answers that you think might be tempting if students are not thinking carefully. For example:

2,897,897 + 37 =
5,000,000   3,000,000   2,000,000   29,000,000

Tell students that you are going to show them an arithmetic problem for only a few seconds. They are to round the numbers in the problem to make them easier to compute with, and estimate the answer.

Note: If an overhead is not available, problems can be written on the board or chart paper.

Step 2. Present the problem, keeping the answers covered, for 20 to 30 seconds. Decrease this time to 15 seconds as students become accustomed to the activity and problem type. It is important not to show the problem so long that students have time to work it out in writing.

Step 3. Cover the problem, and show the choice of answers. Students write down the answer they think is closest. (In the example problem, they might round the numbers to 3,000,000 + 0, or 2,900,000 + 40, and choose 3,000,000 as the closest answer.)

Step 4. Uncover the problem and discuss. One or two students tell how they rounded and why they chose their answer.

Following are some whole-number problems to get you started. Plan to supplement these with problems that you or your students write.

29 + 52 =			
40	60	80	100

545 – 240 =			
200	300	400	700

50,102 – 2898 =			
10,000	20,000	40,000	50,000

32,010 – 934 =			
12,000	23,000	31,000	51,000

36,010 – 19,999 =			
1600	16,000	18,000	56,000

5210 + 298 =			
5400	5500	7000	8000

591,000 + 211,000 =			
700,000	800,000	900,000	10,000,000

3,928,012 – 43 =			
28,000	350,000	3,000,000	4,000,000

3,051,860 + 815 =			
5,000,000	4,000,000	3,000,000	2,000,000

7108 − 141 =			
5000	6000	7000	8000

5982 + 978 =			
6000	7000	14,000	15,000

608 × 980 =			
5000	50,000	600,000	690,000

9 × 211 =			
20	200	2000	20,000

50,300 ÷ 4926 =			
10	1000	10,000	45,000

59 × 11 =			
60	500	600	6000

Variations

Nearest Answer Decimal Problems Students round the decimals to the nearest whole number or, for large numbers, to a landmark number. For example, 527.9 − 2.1321 can be thought of as 528 − 2 or 530 − 0. The accuracy needed will depend on the answer choices. Sample problems:

1.1 × 54 =	5.4	54	540	5400
342 + 0.999 =	14,000	13,000	12,000	340
82 ÷ 4.2 =	0.5	2	20	40
24.8 + 3.1 =	29	28	27	270
498 × 10.13 =	5.00	50.0	500	5000
59.3 × 1.1 =	60	600	6000	60,000
435.4 ÷ 0.98 =	4.4	44	440	4400
268 ÷ 9.9 =	25	250	2.5	2500
402 × 2.96 =	400	800	1200	8000
25 − 2.1 =	4	12	23	30
4.3 − 1.412 =	0	1	3	6
29.93 − 2.1 =	9	20	25	28
80.5 ÷ 3.97 =	4	10	20	80
311 + 3.71 =	11	300	600	800

Nearest Answer Fraction and Mixed Number Problems Students round the fractions to the nearest whole number or, occasionally, to one-half, and estimate. Sample problems:

$8\frac{1}{13} \times 2\frac{9}{11} =$	16	18	24	64
$15\frac{7}{8} + 2\frac{6}{7} =$	17	18	19	29
$5\frac{9}{11} - 2\frac{7}{8} =$	2	3	$3\frac{2}{3}$	32.3
$3\frac{7}{8} + \frac{1}{15} =$	3	4	38.23	50
$\frac{32}{66}$ of 22 =	$\frac{1}{3}$	7	10	45
$\frac{3}{4}$ of 83 =	20	60	240	560
$\frac{3895}{39} =$	0.10	10	100	1000
$\frac{1}{11} + \frac{8}{9} =$	1	2	10	18
$\frac{1}{3} + \frac{4}{7} =$	$\frac{1}{2}$	1	2	3
$\frac{11}{4} =$	0.5	2.8	15	44

Nearest Answer Percent Problems Students use a nearby familiar percent to help them choose an answer. For example, 26% of 77 could be thought of as close to 25% (or 1/4) of 80. Sample problems:

33% of 15.85 =	5	45	450	500
198% of 15 =	7.5	15	30	3000
51% of 69 =	16	35	4	100
98% of 14.3 =	1400	143	14	0.143
25.9% of 774 =	0.2	2	20	200
73% of 406.2 =	50	100	200	300
24% of 83.6 =	2	20	27	100

A bicycle listed at $210 is on sale at a 30% discount. The sale price is about:

$70	$150	$180	$200

With an increase of 10% per year, an article now costing $49 may be expected, in 12 months time, to cost:

$54	$57	$100	$200

Nearest Answer Number Line Problems

A number line is provided with three points labeled—two with numbers, and the third with the letter A. Students decide what number A is nearest to. Sample problems:

2 ———— A ———— 5	A is nearest: 3 3.5 4 4.5

0.7 ———— A 0.8 — A is nearest: 0.6 0.15 0.76 0.79

0 ———— A 1 — A is nearest: −1 $\frac{1}{4}$ $\frac{2}{5}$ $\frac{3}{4}$

−3 ——— −1 ——— A — A is nearest: −5 −2 0 1

6 ———— A 10 — A is nearest: 6 7 8 9

8 ———— A 9 — A is nearest: 8.5 8.21 8.36 8.7

800 ———— A 900 — A is nearest: 8.6 8.7 840 870

580 A ———— 590 — A is nearest: 5.82 58.2 582 5820

Comparing Estimation in Addition and Multiplication
Pose addition and multiplication problems that use the same numbers. Working in pairs, students decide what four or five answers to provide for other students to choose among. They are likely to find that the answers for addition problems cannot range in size as much as answers for multiplication problems if they are still to stump people. For example:

726 + 977 = 1700 1800 1900 8100

726 × 977 = 8400 80,000 700,000 800,000

Looking at the Effects of Rounding Different Factors
Pose multiplication problems with the requirement that students round only one of the factors to a number they can multiply by mentally. Students investigate this using calculators. Which number should they round? By how much can they round and still get a reasonably accurate answer?

Students will probably find that if the factors are close in size, rounding either factor has approximately the same effect. For example, for 38 × 52 [answer 1976], either 38 × 50 or 40 × 52 will give a reasonable approximation. Rounding both numbers to 40 × 50 gives a closer approximation because the numbers are rounded in opposite directions.

However, if the factors are of very different size, rounding the larger factor will result in a closer answer than rounding the smaller number. For example, for 8 × 389 [answer 3112], 8 × 400 produces a closer answer than 10 × 389, even though only 2 was added to the 8, whereas 11 was added to the 389.

Students Invent Their Own Problems
Students prepare problems with a choice of answers. They write about how they would do their own problems. Guide students to use numbers that are near landmark numbers or, in the case of fractions, near whole numbers. At another Ten-Minute Math time, students might exchange their problems with others and compare strategies.

The following activities will help ensure that this unit is comprehensible to students who are acquiring English as a second language. The suggested approach is based on *The Natural Approach: Language Acquisition in the Classroom* by Stephen D. Krashen and Tracy D. Terrell (Alemany Press, 1983). The intent is for second-language learners to acquire new vocabulary in an active, meaningful context.

Note that *acquiring* a word is different from *learning* a word. Depending on their level of proficiency, students may be able to comprehend a word upon hearing it during an investigation, without being able to say it. Other students may be able to use the word orally, but not read or write it. The goal is to help students naturally acquire targeted vocabulary at their present level of proficiency.

We suggest using these activities just before the related investigations. The activities can also be led by English-proficient students.

Investigations 1–2
certain, always, likely, probable, unlikely, low chance, maybe, impossible, never

1. Crumple a piece of paper from the trash can. Put the can right next to you and hold the paper directly over the can, close to rim level. Demonstrate dropping the paper inside. Tell students you were *certain* the paper would fall in the trash can from this distance. And, if you try it again and again this way, you know it will *always* go in.

2. Move the trash can a foot away from you. Explain that it is *likely* or *probable* that the paper will still land inside the trash can when you toss it. Demonstrate.

3. Ask students where you should place the trash can so the paper will *maybe* land inside when tossed, or *maybe not*. Place the can at this distance and let students aim and toss.

4. Now challenge students to decide where the trash can should be placed so that there is a *low chance* the paper will land inside, or it will be *unlikely* to go in. Again, let the students experiment.

5. Finally, ask students to decide where the trash can should be placed so that it is *impossible* to land the paper inside. Place the can in this location and demonstrate that it is impossible. Explain that if you try again and again, the paper will *never* land in the can.

6. Conclude by asking questions that require students to recall the likelihood of landing the paper inside the can from different distances. For example, place the can right next to you and ask:

What are a person's chances of landing the paper inside the can from this distance?

Blackline Masters

_____ , 19 ____

Dear Family,

Our math class is about to start a unit on probability, a subject that appears in our lives in many different forms. When the weather reporter on TV or the radio reports a 70 percent chance of rain, we are being given a probability to help us figure out whether or not to carry an umbrella that day. When we flip a coin to decide who gets to go first in a game, we are using probability. And when we talk about whether someone is likely to have a baby girl or a baby boy, we are also using probability.

Within the next day or so, your child will bring home a sheet on which you both will briefly describe what you think the word _probability_ means. This could lead to an interesting discussion about the many meanings of some words. Another activity your child will be doing at home is tossing a bottle cap many times to see how likely it is to land with the top up. You can help your child keep track of the results of this experiment and try to draw some conclusions from it.

Later, we will be talking about games of skill and games of chance, and how to judge the "fairness" of a game. Listen to your child's explanation of what makes a game fair.

In another homework activity at the end of the unit, your child will experiment with pulling family members' names out of a hat as a fair way of deciding who does a household chore. Although students only pretend to allocate chores this way, you might actually try it out for a while. If you do, be sure to keep track of the results and discuss with your child whether or not it seems fair.

Look and listen for ways probability is being used around you, and discuss these situations with your child. For example, if someone you know has entered a raffle or contest, talk about the probability of winning versus losing. Raise questions like these: About how many people do you think have entered? How many winners will there be? Is there reason to believe your chance of winning is higher or lower than anyone else's chance? These questions are both personally and mathematically interesting and provide important opportunities to "talk mathematics" with your child.

Sincerely,

Name

Date

The Likelihood Line

77

Creating a Likelihood Line (page 1 of 2)

Think about the neighborhood where you live. Can you think of any events in the future that you are certain will happen? Write them down on the likelihood line on page 2 of this student sheet.

Add any events that would be impossible.

Now add a few events that might be *unlikely* to occur, that *maybe* will occur, and that are *likely* to occur. You may want to ask family members or friends to help you think of events and where they might go on the line.

Now write about the questions below.

1. If something is *unlikely*, does it mean it will never happen? What do you think when it does happen?

_____

_____

_____

_____

_____

2. If something is *likely*, does it mean it will always happen? What do you think when it does happen?

_____

_____

_____

_____

_____

Creating a Likelihood Line (page 2 of 2)

certain —+—

likely —+—

maybe —+—

unlikely —+—

impossible —+—

What Is Probability?

Write what you think the word *probability* means.
Give an example. Ask an adult at home to do the same thing.
Compare your answers and talk about them together.

Student

1. What do you think the word *probability* means?

2. Give an example of probability.

Parent or Other Adult

1. What do you think the word *probability* means?

2. Give an example of probability.

Bottle Cap Toss

Find a bottle cap. Try to get a thin, metal one.
Tell what kind of bottle it was on. _____

If you toss a cap, it can land two ways:

Top up     Top down

What do you think the probability is that
the cap will land with the top up? _____

If you toss the cap 50 times, how many times
do you think it will land with the top up? _____

Explain how you came up with this prediction.

Toss the cap 50 times. Record how the cap lands each time.
Then do it again, another 50 times. Record your new data.

First 50 Tosses   **Second 50 Tosses**

Totals for first 50 tosses   Totals for second 50 tosses

Top up _____   Top up _____

Top down _____   Top down _____

Do you still think the probability of top up is what you wrote above? _____

If not, what do you now think the probability is? _____

Guessing Skills Data for Six Classes

Decide whether each line plot is real or made up.
Explain your thinking.

Line plot A

```
              X
              X
              X  X
           X  X  X
        X  X  X  X
     X  X  X  X        X
     X  X  X  X  X  X  X  X
  ─────────────────────────────
  0  1  2  3  4  5  6  7  8  9 10 11
```

Line plot B

```
     X
     X
     X  X
     X  X  X  X
     X  X  X  X
     X  X  X  X        X
     X  X  X  X  X  X  X        X
  ─────────────────────────────
  0  1  2  3  4  5  6  7  8  9 10 11
```

Line plot C

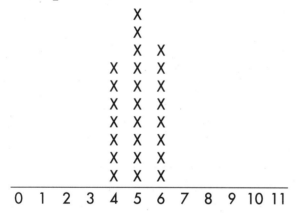

Line plot D

```
           X                 X
           X     X  X  X  X  X
        X  X  X  X  X  X  X  X
        X  X  X  X  X  X  X  X  X
  ─────────────────────────────
  0  1  2  3  4  5  6  7  8  9 10 11
```

Line plot E

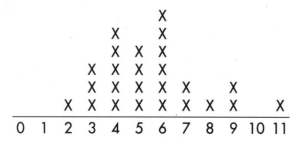

Line plot F

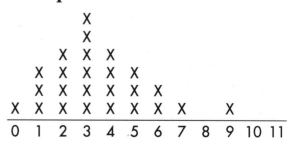

Investigation 1 • Session 6
Between Never and Always

Scoring Options Game (page 1 of 2)

Game A Scoring Options

Circle two of the six options.

You get a point when the spinner lands on

Scoring options you circled	Probability of getting a point
_____	_____
_____	_____

a. a multiple of 5

b. a multiple of 4

c. a factor of 12

d. a factor of 15

e. an odd number

f. a one-digit number

	Spin result	Score
1		
2		
3		
4		
5		
6		
7		
8		
9		
10		
11		
12		
13		
14		
15		
16		
17		
18		
19		
20		
	Total	

Scoring Options Game (page 2 of 2)

Game B Scoring Options

Circle two of the five options.

You get a point when the spinner lands on

a. a multiple of 5

b. a multiple of 10

c. a factor of 40

d. a factor of 45

e. an even number, or one whose digits add up to an even number

Scoring options you circled	Probability of getting a point
_____	_____
_____	_____

	Spin result	Score
1		
2		
3		
4		
5		
6		
7		
8		
9		
10		
11		
12		
13		
14		
15		
16		
17		
18		
19		
20		
	Total	

Scoring Options Challenge (page 1 of 2)

Game C Scoring Options

Circle two of the six options.

You get a point when the spinner lands on

a. a multiple of 7

b. a factor of 42

c. a factor of 27

d. an even number

e. a prime number

f. a square number

	Scoring options you circled	Probability of getting a point
	_____	_____
	_____	_____

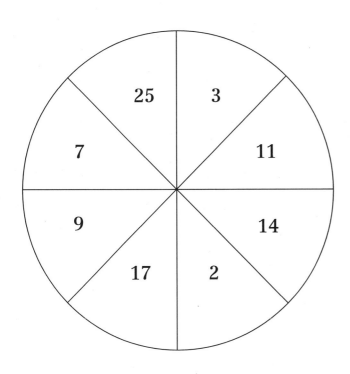

	Spin result	Score
1		
2		
3		
4		
5		
6		
7		
8		
9		
10		
11		
12		
13		
14		
15		
16		
17		
18		
19		
20		
	Total	

Scoring Options Challenge (page 2 of 2)

Game D Scoring Options

Circle two of the five options.

You get a point when the spinner lands on

a. a multiple of 500

b. a multiple of 150

c. a multiple of 100

d. a multiple of 50

e. an odd number

Scoring options you circled

_____

_____

Probability of getting a point

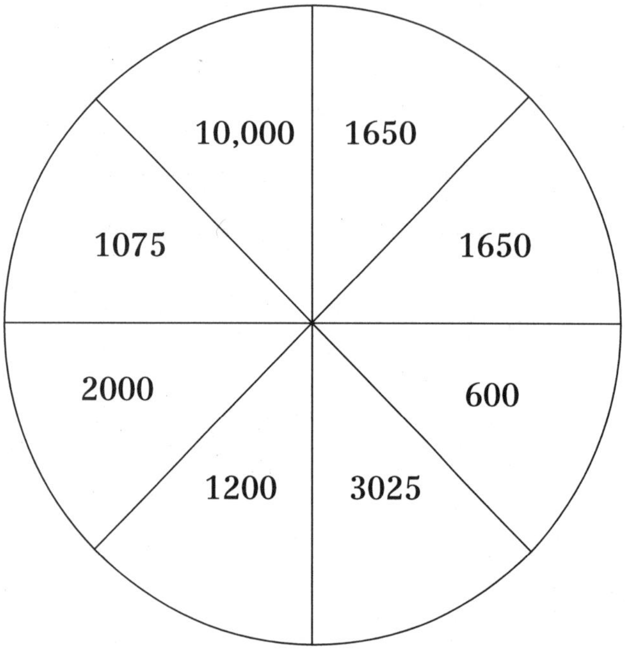

_____

_____

	Spin result	Score
1		
2		
3		
4		
5		
6		
7		
8		
9		
10		
11		
12		
13		
14		
15		
16		
17		
18		
19		
20		
	Total	

Make Your Own Scoring Options

Your Scoring Options

Write six options. Circle two.

You get a point when the spinner lands on

a.

b.

c.

d.

e.

f.

Scoring options you circled	Probability of getting a point
_____	_____
_____	_____

Choose numbers for the spinner.

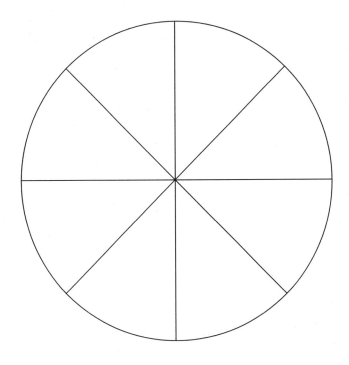

	Spin result	Score
1		
2		
3		
4		
5		
6		
7		
8		
9		
10		
11		
12		
13		
14		
15		
16		
17		
18		
19		
20		
	Total	

SPINNER TEMPLATES

Cut on dotted lines. Each student pair needs just one.

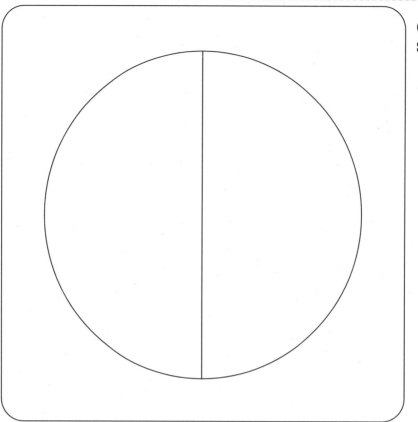

One-half
spinner

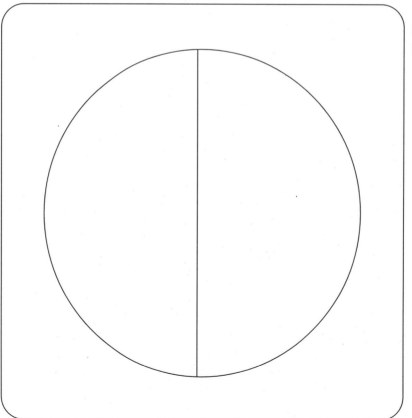

One-half
spinner

Investigation 1 • Resource
Between Never and Always

SPINNER TEMPLATES

Each student pair needs both templates.

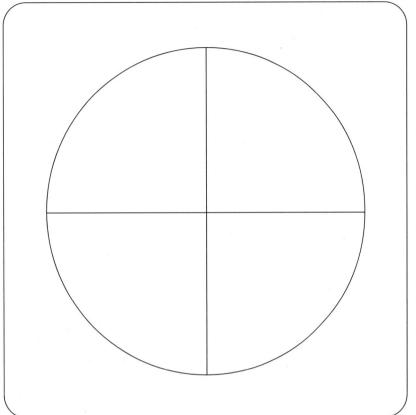

One-fourth
spinner

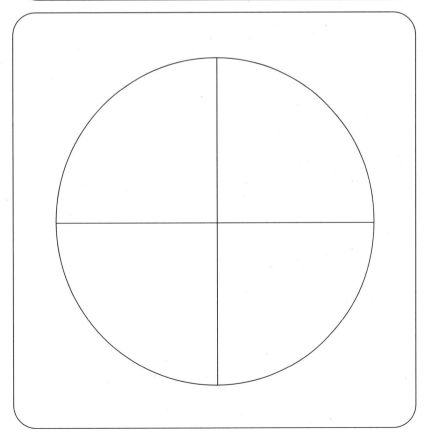

Three-fourths
spinner

89

GUESSING SKILLS SPINNER TEMPLATES

Cut on dotted lines. Each student pair needs just one.

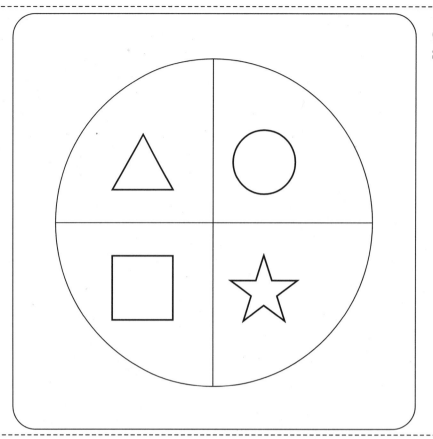

Guessing skills spinner

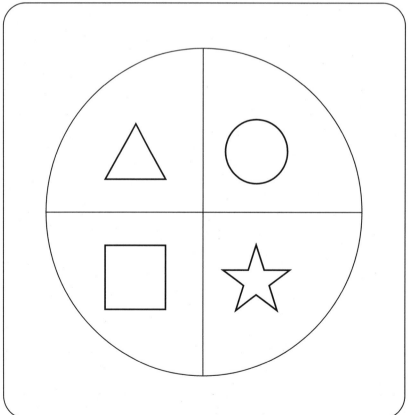

Guessing skills spinner

Games of Skill and Chance

Think about games you know. What is required to win them? Are they games of chance? Does every player have an equal chance of winning? Are they games of skill? Do they involve some combination of chance and skill?

List at least 15 games below. Try to include one or two games for each category.

Games of chance	Games of skill	Games of chance and skill together

Pick one game of chance from your list. On the back of this sheet, explain what makes this a game of chance.

Race to the Top Score Sheet

A	B
START	

A	B
START	

A	B
START	

A	B
START	

A	B
START	

A	B
START	

Deciding Who Goes First

Say you are with friends. You need to decide who goes first in a game. What methods do you use? Tell about them. If you use different methods in different situations, list them all.

Now ask someone of your parents' generation:

"When you were about 10 and you wanted to decide with some friends who went first in a game, what methods did you use? If you used more than one, tell me as many as you can remember."

(Be sure you understand each way well enough so you can explain it to the class.)

Ask someone of your grandparents' generation the same questions.

Assigning Household Jobs

For homework, try out this way of sharing chores.

First, write the name of everybody in your home who is old enough to do chores. Put each name on a separate slip of paper. Don't forget your own name. Put the names in a container.

Now, choose one chore that needs to be done at your home every day (maybe setting the table, taking out the trash, walking the dog, washing the dishes). Each day, you pick a name to decide who does the chore that day.

Pretend to try this system for a month. In one night, pick a name out of the container 31 times, once for each day of the month. Close your eyes when you pick a slip of paper so that you can't see whose name it is.

Be sure to replace the name each time, so that whenever you pick, everyone's name is in the container. Mix up the cards before each pick.

Record your results on the back of this sheet or on another paper. After you have finished, tell the following:

1. How often would each person in your family do the chore during the month?

2. Do you think this is a fair way to decide who does the chore?

3. Do you think it would get more fair or less fair if you used this system for a year?

4. If you don't think this method is fair, make up a method that you do think is fair. Describe it.

UNFAIR SPINNER GAME TEMPLATES

Cut on dotted lines. Each group needs both spinners.

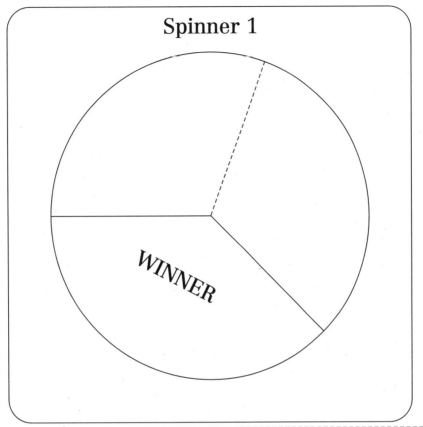

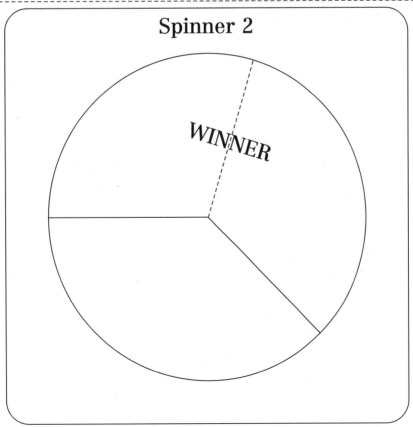

Practice Pages

This optional section provides homework ideas for teachers who want or need to give more homework than is assigned to accompany the activities in this unit. The problems included here provide additional practice in learning about number relationships and in solving computation and number problems. For number units, you may want to use some of these if your students need more work in these areas or if you want to assign daily homework. For other units, you can use these problems so that students can continue to work on developing number and computation sense while they are focusing on other mathematical content in class. We recommend that you introduce activities in class before assigning related problems for homework.

Close to 0 This game is introduced in the unit *Mathematical Thinking at Grade 5*. If your students are familiar with the game, you can simply send home the directions, score sheet, and Numeral Cards so that students can play at home. If your students have not played the game before, introduce it in class and have students play once or twice before sending it home. Students ready for more challenge can try the variation listed at the bottom of the sheet. You might have students do this activity two times for homework in this unit.

Solving Problems in Two Ways Students explore different ways to solve computation problems in the units *Mathematical Thinking at Grade 5* and *Building on Numbers You Know*. Here, we provide two sheets of problems that students solve in two different ways. Problems may include addition, subtraction, multiplication, or division. Students record each way they solved the problem.

Counting Puzzles In this kind of problem, introduced in the unit *Mathematical Thinking at Grade 5*, students are given a clue about a set of numbers. Students find three numbers that match the clue (there may be many numbers that would work). If necessary, you might distribute 300 charts for students to use. Provided here are two problem sheets and one 300 chart, which you can copy for use with the problem sheets. Because this activity is included in the curriculum only as homework, it is recommended that you briefly introduce it in class before students work on it at home.

Close to 0

Materials

- One deck of Numeral Cards
- Close to 0 Score Sheet for each player

Players: 1 or 2

How to Play

1. Deal out eight Numeral Cards to each player.

2. Use any six cards to make two numbers. For example, a 6, a 5, and a 2 could make 652, 625, 526, 562, 256, or 265. Wild Cards can be used as any numeral. Try to make two numbers that, when subtracted, give you a difference that is close to 0.

3. Write these numbers and their difference on the Close to 0 Score Sheet. For example: 652 − 647 = 5. The difference is your score.

4. Put the cards you used in a discard pile. Keep the two cards you didn't use for the next round.

5. For the next round, deal six new cards to each player. Make two more numbers with a difference close to 0. When you run out of cards, mix up the discard pile and use them again.

6. After five rounds, total your scores. Lowest score wins.

Variation   Deal out ten Numeral Cards to each player. Each player uses eight cards to make two numbers that, when subtracted, give a total close to 0.

Close to 0 Score Sheet

Game 1   Score

Round 1:   —— —— —— - —— —— ——   =   ——————   ——————

Round 2:   —— —— —— - —— —— ——   =   ——————   ——————

Round 3:   —— —— —— - —— —— ——   =   ——————   ——————

Round 4:   —— —— —— - —— —— ——   =   ——————   ——————

Round 5:   —— —— —— - —— —— ——   =   ——————   ——————

                                                    TOTAL SCORE   ——————

Game 2   Score

Round 1:   —— —— —— - —— —— ——   =   ——————   ——————

Round 2:   —— —— —— - —— —— ——   =   ——————   ——————

Round 3:   —— —— —— - —— —— ——   =   ——————   ——————

Round 4:   —— —— —— - —— —— ——   =   ——————   ——————

Round 5:   —— —— —— - —— —— ——   =   ——————   ——————

                                                    TOTAL SCORE   ——————

0	0	1	1
0	0	1	1
2	2	3	3
2	2	3	3

Practice Page
Between Never and Always

4	4	5	5
4	4	5	5
<u>6</u>	<u>6</u>	7	7
<u>6</u>	<u>6</u>	7	7

Practice Page
Between Never and Always

8	8	<u>9</u>	<u>9</u>
8	8	<u>9</u>	<u>9</u>
WILD CARD	**WILD CARD**		
WILD CARD	**WILD CARD**		

Practice Page A

Solve this problem in two different ways, and write about
how you solved it:

24 × 19 =

Here is the first way I solved it:

Here is the second way I solved it:

Practice Page B

Solve this problem in two different ways, and write about how you solved it:

145 ÷ 12 =

Here is the first way I solved it:

Here is the second way I solved it:

300 CHART

1	2	3	4	5	6	7	8	9	10
11	12	13	14	15	16	17	18	19	20
21	22	23	24	25	26	27	28	29	30
31	32	33	34	35	36	37	38	39	40
41	42	43	44	45	46	47	48	49	50
51	52	53	54	55	56	57	58	59	60
61	62	63	64	65	66	67	68	69	70
71	72	73	74	75	76	77	78	79	80
81	82	83	84	85	86	87	88	89	90
91	92	93	94	95	96	97	98	99	100
101	102	103	104	105	106	107	108	109	110
111	112	113	114	115	116	117	118	119	120
121	122	123	124	125	126	127	128	129	130
131	132	133	134	135	136	137	138	139	140
141	142	143	144	145	146	147	148	149	150
151	152	153	154	155	156	157	158	159	160
161	162	163	164	165	166	167	168	169	170
171	172	173	174	175	176	177	178	179	180
181	182	183	184	185	186	187	188	189	190
191	192	193	194	195	196	197	198	199	200
201	202	203	204	205	206	207	208	209	210
211	212	213	214	215	216	217	218	219	220
221	222	223	224	225	226	227	228	229	230
231	232	233	234	235	236	237	238	239	240
241	242	243	244	245	246	247	248	249	250
251	252	253	254	255	256	257	258	259	260
261	262	263	264	265	266	267	268	269	270
271	272	273	274	275	276	277	278	279	280
281	282	283	284	285	286	287	288	289	290
291	292	293	294	295	296	297	298	299	300

Practice Page
Between Never and Always

Practice Page C

Find three numbers that fit each clue.

1. If you count by this number, you will say 48, but you will not say 50.

2. If you count by this number, you will say 280, but you will not say 260.

3. If you count by this number, you will say 80, but you will not say 90.

Practice Page D

Find three numbers that fit each clue.

1. If you count by this number, you will say 135, but you will not say 140.

2. If you count by this number, you will say 105, but you will not say 100.

3. If you count by this number, you will say 175, but you will not say 180.